"This is one of the more beautifully designed, thoughtful, insightful, inspirational, and useful journals for creating a happy, fulfilling, and productive life that I have ever seen. I highly recommend it."

—JACK CANFIELD, Coauthor of the #1 New York Times bestselling *Chicken Soup for the Soul* series, *The Success Principles*™, and a featured teacher in *The Secret*

"What a jewel! *I'm Great Every Day* is a rich overview of seven key principles of personal growth and a helpful tool for practical daily application. Linda Callahan is clearly steeped in personal growth and it shows. She is a wise guide with a gentle way of distilling core elements into bite-size chunks. *I'm Great Every Day* will shave a decade off the learning curve for someone new to the path of personal development, and in a short time, will yield a bounty of fruit to inspire them to keep going. I love how this book is so thoughtfully designed. Linda briefly tells us why each element is important, giving us the strong incentive to immediately implement each principle into our daily ritual. And then she gives us a concise format to do just that. *I'm Great Every Day* is a thoughtful gift for new travelers on this path, while also serving up needed reminders for seasoned seekers. This book brings much joy. In itself, it is a living affirmation. Well done! Highly recommend!"

—ANGELA HOWELL, Author of *Finding the Gift: Daily Meditations for Mindfulness*

"What we loved about *I'm Great Every Day* is that it's great for someone new to journaling and working to find their path. Even if you are someone who journals daily, this well-rounded approach beginning with intention is really helpful to make sure you are getting the most out of your daily routine. Where the mind goes the energy flows, and this book creates a beautiful routine to keep your mind on your chosen path."

—TOM AND KELLY GAINES, Founders of Pink Zebra Home

I'M GREAT
Every Day

A Guided Journal *for* Creating *a* Better Self

Linda Callahan

LINDA CALLAHAN

TRANQUIL SOULS
PUBLISHING

Published by Tranquil Souls Publishing
First Edition, March 2021

Publishing and Design Services: Melinda Martin, MartinPublishingServices.com

ISBN: 978-0-578-86052-7 (paperback)

This book is dedicated to my husband Dave,
who has always encouraged me, inspired me,
and believed in my dream of becoming a writer,

to my children Jennifer, Michael, and Megan,
that they will always be inspired to pursue their own dreams,
no matter where their dreams may take them,

and

to all of those who had the courage to chase their dreams
and turn them into a reality.

This book is for you.

Introduction

Hello, fellow journal friends! Thank you for purchasing *I'M GREAT Every Day: A Guided Journal for Creating a Better Self.* If you love journaling as much as I do, then you are going to love this journal. What I love most about this journal is that it's an all-inclusive journal; everything you need to say can be written in this one book. You'll have the opportunity to respond to a given prompt, record your daily intentions, jot down what you're grateful for each day, record your reading notes, your exercise routine, your affirmations, and even what you did each day to make your soul happy. You will no longer need to shuffle from one journal to another. Having the convenience of needing only one journal to record all of your writings will not only make your writing experience easier, but you will once again fall in love with the art of writing.

Before creating this journal, I used to write in several journals simultaneously. I had my gratitude journal, my habit tracking journal, my meditation journal, my prompted journal, and of course, my daily journal. Even for someone who loves writing, this was just too many journals. I wanted something simpler. I wanted a journal where everything could be contained in one place. And so, I got to work designing a journal that would work for me.

After I finished creating it, I fell in love with its simplicity. I loved having one journal to record all of my daily writings. If this journal was making life easier for me, then I knew others would appreciate its simplicity as well. And that, my friends, is how *I'M GREAT Every Day: A Guided Journal for Creating a Better Self* was born.

PART
one

The Story Behind

I'M GREAT

Every Day

A Guided Journal for Creating a Better Self

And suddenly you know it's time to start something new and trust the magic of beginnings.

-MEISTER ECKHART

The Story Behind

I'M GREAT

Every Day

A Guided Journal for Creating a Better Self

Go confidently in the direction of your dreams. Live the life you have imagined.

-HENRY DAVID THOREAU

One of the most influential books I have ever read was *The Artist's Way* by Julia Cameron. In her book, Julia recommends starting every day with what she calls her *morning pages*. Since I've always been the type of person that prefers to start the day with a routine, I couldn't wait to implement my own morning pages into my daily routine. After a few days of writing my morning pages, I realized these pages were instrumental in helping me begin each day on a positive note.

Once I made the decision to include writing as part of my morning routine, I began to look for other forms of writing to include. I was already using several journals, such as *The Five Minute Journal* and *The Mindfulness Journal* on a daily basis. I was especially fond of the *Be Inspired* journal and other self-discovery reflection journals because I was learning so much about myself through my responses.

In addition to the above journals, I also kept a gratitude journal. Besides writing about what I was grateful for each day, I would also use these pages to record my daily intentions, affirmations, and an inspirational quote. The more I continued to write in my gratitude journal, the more grateful I became. Keeping a gratitude journal was helping me become a more positive person.

Journaling soon became a way of life. I even started keeping a separate habit tracking journal so I could cross off each morning activity as I completed it. A few weeks later, I made the decision to add exercise to my routine. Along with exercising, I was now making time every day to do something that would feed my soul, whether it be a walk on the beach, time spent with loved ones or friends, a relaxing day at the spa, or whatever else I might want to do to make my soul happy. I made sure to do something every day to fulfill each section in my habit tracking journal.

Being retired from my career as an elementary teacher left me plenty of time to pursue my love for reading. I especially love reading personal development books because I truly believe that we should continually strive to become a better version of ourselves. One of my favorite reads was *The Miracle Morning: The Not-So-Obvious Secret Guaranteed to Transform Your Live (Before 8AM)* by Hal Elrod. After reading his book, I knew I'd want to add some reading time to my current morning routine.

Shortly after my retirement, a friend introduced me to *Oprah Winfrey and Deepak Chopra's 21 Day Meditations.* Listening to their mediation and their inspiring words of wisdom, I found myself looking forward to a few moments of silence every morning. It was right around this time, that a friend of mine, Sylvia, invited me to enroll in her class, *Practical Meditations.* Her class was phenomenal and I knew then that I would want to incorporate meditation into my morning routine. Wanting to keep track of the amount of time I meditated daily, I added the app *Insight Timer* to my phone. *Insight Timer* is a wonderful app that not only tracks how often you meditate, but also provides you with different types of guided meditations.

My new morning ritual now included several different activities. I was now journaling in several different journals, meditating, exercising, reading, and recording my daily intentions and affirmations. I was also taking notes on what I was reading every day and recording the activities I was doing each day to feed my soul.

After a few days, I found it difficult to keep up with all the journals. If I wanted to be successful with my new routine, I would need to find a simpler way to record everything. What I needed was one journal that could incorporate all of my writing needs. So I began scouring the internet looking for that one journal that would work for me. Although I found many great journals, I couldn't find exactly what I was looking for. That's when I knew I'd have to create my own journal. Once I had the idea to write a journal, I knew I'd want to include a section for every activity that I was now completing on a daily basis. I became so inspired by this idea, that I was able to complete the first draft of the book you are now reading in just a few months.

After just a few short weeks of practicing my new routine, I noticed a positive change in myself. I was now waking up each morning eager to see what gifts the new day would bring. I found myself having more energy throughout the day, and I was feeling more at peace with myself at the end of the day. My new routine was making a positive impact on my life. My days now had a purpose.

When it came time to title my book, I knew I'd want to create a title that would somehow reflect all the activities I was now performing on a daily basis. In order to do this, I would need to find a clever way to incorporate each component of my morning routine which now included my daily intention, meditation, gratitude, reading, exercising and affirmations. I was also taking time every day for self-care knowing it was just as important to nourish my soul as it was to nourish my body and my mind. My new routine was helping me to feel GREAT each and every day.

Still looking for inspiration for a title, I listed my morning activities in vertical order on a blank sheet of paper. When I took a second look at what I had just written, I noticed that the first letter of each activity spelled out the words I'M GREAT! These two words not only captured the essence of how I felt each morning after completing my morning routine, but they would also be a great title for my book. I could also use these two words as a positive mantra to begin each day. My inner voice suggested adding the words *Every Day* to the title. I knew that if I continued to practice these activities every day, I could create a better version of myself. If performing these practices every day were helping me to feel better about myself, then maybe they would be beneficial in helping others who were also looking to make a similar change in their lives.

What is the best way to use this book?

This journal was designed for the creative writer in all of us. As you complete each of the daily practices, feel free to personalize your journal as you see fit. You might want to add quotes and doodles on each page to make this journal uniquely yours.

I prefer to journal in the morning because it's a positive way for me to begin my day. It's also easier for me to write in the morning because I haven't yet had the opportunity to experience any distractions and /or obligations that the day is sure to bring. I am more focused in the morning so that's when I choose to write.

Before you embark on your journey of personal development, let's take a look as to how this journal is organized. This book has been divided into six parts. At the end of each section, you'll have the opportunity to reflect on the section of the journey you've just completed. Take as much time as you need to reflect on the changes you've seen in yourself. Whenever you are ready to move on, the next section will be waiting for you.

In Part 1, which is what you're reading now, I've explained how you can best use this book so that you can make the ultimate transformation as you journey through it.

In Part 2, you'll find a brief description for each activity that I've included in my daily routine, along with the benefits that can result from practicing these activities on a daily basis. You'll also find a journal prompt that corresponds to each activity. At the end of each of these mini-chapters, I included a notetaking page. Feel free to use this page as you see fit.

Your journey of self-discovery will take you through Parts 3, 4, and 5. Each of these sections will provide you with thirty days of self-discovery. At the beginning of each of these thirty-day sections, you will have the opportunity to set a goal for the month ahead. After setting your goal, you'll create a vision board to help manifest the goal you have chosen. You'll also be provided with daily prompts and fun activities to help you find your authentic self. One of my favorite activities in Part 3 is the *I AM* page. These two little words, although small in size, have the power to drastically transform your life.

Each day you will respond to a given prompt, set your intention for the day, reflect on your meditation, and write down what you are grateful for. There will be a place for you to keep notes on the material you are reading along with a place to track your exercise. Each day you will create daily affirmations for yourself. Our words have the power to change us. Positive affirmations and visualizations can help you become the person you've always wanted to be. You'll also have a place to record what you did that day to feed your soul.

In Part 6, your transformational journey will come to a close. In this final section, you'll be able to reflect on your entire journey. As the author of this book, I can only hope that your journey through this journal will be as transformative for you as it was for me.

Thank you once again for choosing *I'M GREAT Every Day: A Guided Journal for Creating a Better Self* as part of your self-discovery journey.

PART
two

Intention

*You create your thoughts. Your thoughts create your intentions
and your intentions create your reality.*

-WAYNE DYER

Intention

*Living with intention means saying no to the things that aren't important to us
so that we can say yes to what matters most.*

-CRYSTAL PAINE

Intention is the conscious awareness of a thought or action that you plan to carry out. When you live with intention, every thought, action, and choice you make is purposely performed to align with the beliefs that are most important to you. Intentional living simply means living a life with purpose.

John C. Maxwell, well-known motivational speaker and author of *Intentional Living: Choosing a Life that Matters,* defines intentional living in this way, "When you get right down to it, intentional living is about living your best story." John goes on to say, "If you want to live a life that matters, don't start when you get good; start now so you become good."

Linda Ellis, author of *The Dash: Making a Difference with Your Life from Beginning to End and Live Your Dash: Make Every Moment Matter,* and the world famous poem "*The Dash*" explains the significance of the dash between the day you were born and the day you died. The dash between these two dates represents the life you lived while on this green earth. Ellis challenges each of us to think about the dash in our life: *When your time on earth is over, what will your dash say about the life you lived?*

When you live a life with intention, you bring meaning to your dash. We are only on this good earth for a short period of time. When it comes time for your eulogy to be read, how do you want to be remembered? Today, make a promise to yourself to start living your life with intention so that when your eulogy is read, others will be aspired to live up to the memory of your dash. Live your life so that every moment counts; make your life legendary. *I do not mind being ordinary. 1/2/22*

Why should you begin your morning with an intention?

When you deliberately begin your day with a positive intention, you're not only holding yourself accountable for how your day will play out, but you will also be more mindful of the choices you make during the day. When you intentionally focus every thought and action on that intention, it becomes easier for you to manifest your desire.

What is the benefit to beginning your day with intention?

When we deliberately live our life with a concentrated effort on the values that are important to our well-being and spiritual growth, we grow more centered, more grounded, and more at peace. Living a life with intention gives our life purpose; allowing us the opportunity to grow into a better person from the person we were the day before.

Your daily intention is the seed of your day, a seed that has the potential to change the outcome of your life. Ask yourself: *Who am I? Who do I want to become? What am I longing for? What seeds do I need to plant today in order to become that person?*

Intention

Intentional living means making choices for your life
based on your greatest values, not the habits of others.

- BRIAN BUFFINI

Which values are most important to you? What are you intentionally doing each day to instill these values into your daily life?

_____

_____

_____

_____

_____

_____

_____

_____

_____

_____

_____

_____

_____

_____

_____

_____

_____

_____

Notes

Meditation

Quiet the mind and the soul will speak.

-Ma Jaya Sate Bhagavati

Meditation

The goal of meditation isn't to control your thoughts,
it's to stop letting them control you.

-Anonymous

Meditation is a state of awareness, a time for stillness to focus on one's breathing in the present moment. Its purpose is to find inner peace and contentment.

No one knows exactly when the practice of meditation originated, but it is believed to have started as far back as 5,000 - 3,000 BCE. The earliest records of meditation date back to 1500 BCE. Deepak Chopra, one of the world's top experts on the practice of meditation, says, "Meditation is a state of yoga, wherein we silence our thought process and arrive at the source of thought. In other words, we mantle notions of the self and arrive at a higher being. Meditation is a process of calming the mind and an affirmation of the individual relationship to the universal."

Shyalpa Tenzin Rinpoche, another world famous spiritual leader, was born in the hills of the Himalaya Mountains and was first recognized as a holy child at the age of four. It was at this age that he began his training as a lama, an honorary title for a spiritual leader in Tibetan Buddhism. Rinpoche has defined meditation as a practice for more than just relaxation. "Its primary purpose is to develop the capacity to respond skillfully and gracefully to life's difficulties as well as its joys."

Thich Nhat Hanh, a world renowned Vietnamese Buddhist monk and peace activist says, "Meditation is not to escape from society, but to come back to ourselves and see what is going on. Once there is seeing, there must be acting. With mindfulness, we know what to do and what not to do to help."

When I asked my friend Sylvia Lockwood, the coach of *Practical Meditation,* what meditation meant to her, she said, "Meditation allows the very best parts of ourselves to rise to the surface of our awareness where we can then share these gifts of love, compassion, inspiration, and grace with ourselves, our loved ones and the world."

No matter which definition you believe in, true meditation is an ongoing practice. It takes a disciplined mind to ignore the distracting thoughts that attempt to divert our attention during a meditation period, but with regular practice, you'll begin to appreciate the benefits of meditation.

Why should you practice meditation?

If we truly want to relax our bodies, we must first learn how to quiet our thoughts. Meditation, when practiced consistently, will help to relax both your mind and your body.

In our constantly busy world, we seldom take time to just *be*. We are always doing, always moving, always rushing from one activity to the next. We don't take the time to rest in between the activities that we deem so important. The chatter in our minds keeps us in a constant state of motion. Meditation, however, provides us with the mental break we so desperately need.

Many people argue that they do not have enough time to meditate; they have too much to do and cannot afford the time to sit and just be still. But there is an ancient Zen saying that says, "You should sit in meditation for twenty minutes a day unless you're too busy. Then you should sit for an hour."

Meditation has been studied for centuries in many parts of the world, but the Western civilization is just beginning to appreciate the benefits of meditation. Educators, neuroscientists, and psychologists that have been studying its effects on school age students are finding meditation improves not only the academic skills of the students, but also their social skills. Anti-social behaviors are on the decline for those students who are allowed to meditate daily as part of their curriculum. It also has a positive effect on the students because it teaches them to be compassionate toward others and improves their self-esteem. Imagine how much better our world would be if schools and businesses alike provided time for daily meditation.

When you allow meditation to become a part of your daily routine, you'll find it's easier to accomplish everything you need to do because you've given your mind and body time to replenish. Even just a few minutes of daily meditation can be enough to renew your energy.

If you add meditation to your daily routine, I would suggest creating a sacred place where you can meditate. It does not need to be a large space; something as small as a table can suffice. Next, fill your personal space with items that are meaningful to you. Consider adding some candles, statues, some family photos or anything else that holds meaning for you.

What are the benefits to meditating?

Meditation is so much more than quieting the mind. A daily practice will not only reduce the stress in your life and lower your blood pressure, but it's been shown to generate a feeling of optimism, which can improve both your confidence and your self-esteem. Since meditation is a time to be still and observe, many people who have made the commitment to sit in silence for even a few minutes a day have noticed an improvement in their problem-solving skills. Sitting in silence offers them the opportunity to reflect. As a result, they are able to find new solutions to their problems.

Meditation

The answers you seek never come when the mind is busy;
they come when the mind is still, when silence speaks the loudest.

-ANONYMOUS

Have you practiced meditation before or is meditation new to you? What are your thoughts on meditation? Describe how you feel during meditation. Has your meditation practice changed since you first started your practice? Did any of the answers you were seeking come to you during your time of silence? If so, explain.

_____

_____

_____

_____

_____

_____

_____

_____

_____

_____

_____

_____

_____

_____

_____

_____

Notes

Gratitude

It is not joy that makes us grateful; it is gratitude that makes us joyful.

-ANONYMOUS

Gratitude

Your living is determined not so much by what life brings to you as by the attitude you bring to life; not so much by what happens to you as by the way your mind looks at what happens.

-Khalil Gibran

When speaking of gratitude, American author Melody Beattie, says, "Gratitude unlocks the fullness of life. It turns what we have into enough, and more. It turns denial into acceptance, chaos to order, confusion to clarity. It can turn a meal into a feast, a house into a home, a stranger into a friend. Gratitude makes sense of our past, brings peace for today and creates a vision for tomorrow."

When we live our life with gratitude, it becomes easier for us to accept our past, to be at peace in the present moment, and gives us a reason to look forward to tomorrow.

Why is it important to cultivate an attitude of gratitude?

Research has already proven that plants thrive when they are spoken to in a positive manner. Like plants, people also thrive when they are treated with love and kindness. This is why it's important to cultivate an attitude of gratitude.

One of the best ways to begin your day with gratitude is to start your day with a positive thought. When I begin my morning with a positive thought, it becomes easier for me to maintain my positive attitude throughout the day even though situations may arise to challenge me. Some of my favorite morning thoughts are:

- Today is a new day. Anything is possible.
- Believe that something wonderful will happen today.
- Do something today that will make yesterday jealous.
- Do something today that your future self will thank you for.

Throughout the day, take time to weed out your negative thoughts and worries. Eliminating these negative thoughts will make it easier for your positive thoughts to thrive. When we cultivate an attitude of gratitude, we fill our lives with many beautiful blooms.

At the end of your day, take time to harvest the blessings that the day has given you. Say *I love you* to the people that matter most to you. Spend time doing the things that bring you joy. At the end of day, take time to count your blessings by writing them down in your gratitude journal. In counting your blessings, you'll realize how blessed you truly are. Appreciating your gifts will allow more gifts to come your way and will bring you inner peace.

What are the benefits of being grateful?

Being grateful is a choice. In addition to bringing inner peace, gratitude has many other surprising benefits. Cultivating an attitude of gratitude may lower your stress level and improve your physical and mental health. People who practice gratitude not only tend to live longer, but also tend to be more successful in life and have stronger ties with their community.

Gratitude is contagious; a grateful person inspires others to appreciate even the simplest things. In a world where we can be anything, let's choose to be kind. Let the kindness you share today become the ripples for tomorrow's acts of kindness. Live your life with a grateful heart.

Gratitude

Choosing to be positive and having a grateful attitude
is going to determine how you're going to live your life.

-Joel Osteen

What are you grateful for this morning? How can adopting an attitude of gratitude make a positive difference in your life today?

_____

_____

_____

_____

_____

_____

_____

_____

_____

_____

_____

_____

_____

_____

_____

_____

_____

_____

_____

_____

Notes

Reading

The more that you read, the more things you will know.
The more things that you learn, the more places you'll go.

-DR. SEUSS

Reading

The journey of a lifetime starts with the turning of a page.

-RACHEL ANDERS

Just about any answer you may need in life can be found within the pages of a book. Reading can be a source of entertainment or it can be informative, depending on the type of books you choose to read. I particularly love reading personal development books because I learn so much about myself while reading them. At the end of this book, I've included a list of some of my favorite personal development books that you might want to check out for yourself.

Why is reading important?

Reading is technically defined as a multifaceted process comprised of several interrelated cognitive skills used to understand a written language. But to me, reading is so much more than this technical definition. It's a magical gateway that opens the doors to our creativity and fuels our imagination. Reading is our passport to new worlds. It allows us the opportunity to visit places from the past, the present and the future all without having to leave the comfort of our chair.

What are the benefits of reading?

A steady diet of reading stimulates the brain and improves our memory and concentration. In addition, reading on a steady basis helps to improve both your vocabulary and your writing skills. Reading develops the imagination and increases creativity. Fluent readers are often articulate speakers, making it easier for them to be successful in their careers. Most importantly, reading provides us with new knowledge.

So what are you waiting for? Make yourself a cup of tea, grab yourself a book, and snuggle up with a cozy blanket. You'll soon discover that there's no place better to be than between the pages of a good book.

Reading

The world belongs to those who read.

Is reading something you enjoy or something you struggle with? Is there a particular genre that you prefer to read? Do you have a favorite author or book? If so, explain how your favorite author or book has made a positive impact on your life.

_____

_____

_____

_____

_____

_____

_____

_____

_____

_____

_____

_____

_____

_____

_____

_____

_____

_____

Notes

Exercise

Exercise is the most underutilized antidepressant.

-BILL PHILLIPS

Exercise

Exercise not only changes your body.
It changes your mind, your attitude, and your mood.

-ANONYMOUS

When speaking of optimal health, the World Health Organization says, "Health is a state of complete physical, mental, and social well-being, and not merely the absence of disease or infirmity." When you exercise, your body produces more serotonin, a critical neurotransmitter located in the brain that is responsible for optimal health and well-being.

Why should one exercise daily?

Our bodies are our temples. If we want to live our lives to the fullest, then we need to do whatever we can to keep our bodies functioning at its best. A healthy diet and exercise are crucial to maintain our health.

Exercise requires physical exertion to be carried out, especially to sustain or improve health and fitness. It's a necessary element to living a healthy life. Everybody should participate in some form of daily exercise. Before beginning any new form of exercise, it's always a good idea to check in with your physician or health care provider.

Most people prefer to exercise in the morning because it gives them a sense of renewed energy for the rest of the day. If you can't find the time in the morning to exercise, then by all means exercise whenever your schedule allows for it. The most important thing is to do it daily in whatever form of exercise that works best for you.

What are the benefits that come from a daily exercise routine?

Daily exercise benefits the mind and body in many ways. Exercising regularly will help you maintain a healthy body. It will also help maintain your ideal weight or assist you in losing those unwanted pounds. Regular exercise will also help you to sleep better.

Exercise is also elemental in healing the body. A daily ritual of physical activity decreases a person's risk of developing certain illnesses, such as diabetes and high blood pressure. When we exercise, our bodies also produce endorphins, a chemical produced by the nervous system to reduce pain and stress. These same endorphins also act as natural anti-depressants because they promote a feeling of happiness.

So let's make today the beginning of a healthier you. Start a daily exercise routine today that works with your schedule.

Exercise

Take care of your body. It's the only place you have to live in.

-JIM ROHN

Do you exercise on a regular basis? If not, what can you do today to start adding exercise into your daily routine? If you do exercise, explain how exercising has made a positive difference in your life. Do you prefer to exercise at home or at a gym? What type of exercise do you enjoy the most?

_____

_____

_____

_____

_____

_____

_____

_____

_____

_____

_____

_____

_____

_____

_____

_____

_____

Notes

Affirmations

It's the repetition of affirmations that lead to belief. And once that belief becomes a deep conviction, things begin to happen.

-Muhammad Ali

Affirmations

One comes to believe whatever one repeats to oneself sufficiently often, whether the statement be true or false. It comes to be the dominating thought in one's mind.

-ROBERT COLLIER

While affirmations can be negative or positive, positive affirmations can be a very powerful tool in helping you achieve what you most desire.

Our thoughts are powerful and they have the power to change us. If we can change how we think of ourselves and begin to see ourselves in a more positive way, we can become a better version of who we are. If we can change our thoughts, we can change our lives.

Why have daily affirmations?

When you repeat an affirmation to yourself, whether negative or positive, your subconscious mind begins to believe what it is hearing and works hard to fulfill that statement.

For example, if you continuously tell yourself that you're a failure, things will happen in your life to fulfill that thought. As a result, you will become the failure you believed yourself to be simply because you've manifested a self-fulfilled prophecy.

On the other hand, if you repeat positive thoughts about yourself, your subconscious is going to work just as hard to make sure you become that person. This is why it is of the upmost importance that your affirmations be positive and uplifting.

Henry Ford said it best when he said, "Whether you think you can or you think you can't, either way you're right."

How to write affirmations

There are several guidelines you need to follow when you write affirmations:

- **Start your affirmations with the words *I am* or *I have*.** When the subconscious hears the words *I am* or *I have,* it hears those words as a demand and does what it needs to do to make it happen.

    > *I am* capable of accomplishing everything I set out to do.
    > *I have* everything I need in order to be successful.

- **Always write your affirmations in the present tense.** If you write your affirmations in the future tense, *I will,* that is exactly where they will stay; in the future and unobtainable.

- **Write your affirmation as a positive statement.** State what you want, not what you *don't want.* The subconscious does not understand the word *no.* When writing your affirmation, be as specific as you can so you receive exactly what you desire. Believe what you want is already yours.

    Instead of this: I don't want to fail my test today.
    Write this: I am going to pass my test today because I studied hard and I know the material I am about to be tested on.

    Instead of this: Someday I want to travel somewhere warm.
    Write this: This winter, I am going to be relaxing in a beach chair in Hawaii soaking up the sun's rays.

    The important thing is to not worry about *how* something is going to happen, just believe that it will happen. The Universe will take care of the how.

- **Affirmations need to be written for you, not someone else.** Remember that you are trying to change your behavior, not the behaviors of anyone else. Your affirmations are only going to work for you.

- Always add the words *or something better* to your affirmation.

    Instead of this: I am looking for a new job that will pay me 20% more than my current job is paying me.
    Write this: I am looking for employment with a company that will raise my annual salary by 20% or even better.

- **Keep your affirmations short and sweet.** Allow your affirmations to become your new mantras and repeat them often. Make your affirmations visible. Post them on your refrigerator, mirror, or computer screen. Write them on index cards and read them often during the day. Record them on your phone and listen to them whenever you can. The important thing is to say your affirmations often. The more your subconscious hears them, the harder it will work to turn your dreams into your reality.

Remember, you will become who you believe yourself to be.

What are the benefits of positive affirmations?

Your thoughts have the power to change you. If you want a life that is different from the life you are now living, then you need to change your thoughts. Changing your thoughts can make a huge impact on how you view yourself and the world around you.

Wake up every morning and tell yourself how wonderful you are. Repeat that thought often. If you need to, stand in front of your vanity mirror, and repeat the following words: I am amazing. I am strong. I am healthy. I am worthy. I am grateful for all that I have. I am happy being me. I am kind. I am able to accomplish anything I set out to do. I am beautiful just the way I am. I am becoming a better version of myself every day. I AM ENOUGH!!

In time, this positive self-talk will begin to take form and soon you'll see a different reflection looking back at you. You'll see a better version of yourself; someone who is stronger, confident, and happier. Embrace that new self.

A morning routine that includes positive affirmations allows you become the person you were always destined to be. Studies have shown that people who practice daily affirmations tend to be happier, and more successful. When you possess a positive self-image, it becomes easier to project that positive attitude to everything else happening in your world. Your positivity will inspire those around you to become more positive.

Affirmations are empowering! By believing that you are capable of achieving whatever it is you desire, you open yourself up to even more possibilities than you could have ever imagined. Go now, and become the person you were always meant to be.

Affirmations

Thinking positive thoughts will always empower you.
Think them enough and they will change your life.

-ANONYMOUS

Write a list of affirmations most important to you. Make several copies of this page and put these affirmations in places where you see them and can read them often.

_____

_____

_____

_____

_____

_____

_____

_____

_____

_____

_____

_____

_____

_____

_____

_____

_____

_____

_____

Notes

Time for Self-Care

It's not selfish to love yourself, take care of yourself,
and to make your happiness a priority. It's necessary.

-MANDY HALS

Time for Self-Care

Take time to do what makes your soul happy.

-ANONYMOUS

"Self-care is, fundamentally, about bringing balance back to a life that has grown imbalanced from too many commitments or responsibilities," says author Robyn L. Gobin in her book *The Self-Care Prescription.*

Melody Beattie, author of *Journey to the Heart,* defines self-love in this way, "Self-love means loving and accepting yourself, your thoughts, beauty, emotions, your faults, imperfections, and flaws, your strengths, wit, wisdom, as well as your peculiar and unique way of seeing the world. Loving yourself means accepting and loving each and every part of you, and knowing – knowing– that you're worthy, valuable, and lovable."

If you really want to live a healthier life, you need to love yourself enough to put your needs first. Ask yourself, *What do I need in this moment? Do I need a few minutes alone, do I need to walk away from a relationship or a job, do I need a fresh start, is there something or someone I need to let go of in order to move forward?* Once you have the answer to these questions, then do whatever it takes to insure that your needs are met.

Making time for yourself is an important necessity in living a healthy life. When you make time for your well-being, you give your mind, body, and spirit the time it needs to recharge. Knowing how important self-care is to our emotional and physical well-being, why then do so few of us take this time for ourselves?

The reason is because rather than focusing on our own needs, we mistakenly make the needs of everyone else our priority.

Let's face it; we live in an extremely hectic world. We're constantly racing against the clock in an attempt to complete everything on our never-ending list of things to do. But we're so busy micromanaging everything that we need do to in order to please our family, our friends, our boss and our co-workers that we feel selfish when we consider our own needs.

So, how do we fix this problem and make time for ourselves?

How do I make time for myself?

If you really want to make more time for yourself, the first thing you'll need to do is to change your thinking. Taking care of your needs is not a luxury; it is a necessity. In order to make your needs a priority, you need to take control of your life. Keep reminding yourself that you are worthy of this time.

Mental health is a growing concern in today's extremely chaotic society. If we are to remain happy, then it's up to us to make our needs our priority. Take the time to really listen to what your body, mind, and heart need and then act on it.

There will always be someone or something demanding your attention. We often have the false conception that we are only deserving of "me time" after everything else on our never ending chore list is done. This kind of thinking can be detrimental to your health. If you want to live a healthier life, you'll have to put your needs ahead of everyone else.

Thich Nhat Hanh, a Vietnamese Buddhist monk and peace activist says, "If we do not know how to take care of ourselves and to love ourselves, we cannot take care of the people we love. Loving oneself is the foundation of loving another person."

When we care enough about ourselves to give ourselves that much needed break, we're able to give a much better version of ourselves to others. Self-love is not selfish. So make time for that bubble bath, spend time in nature, enjoy a solitary walk, spend some time practicing meditation or yoga, pursue a hobby or spend time with a friend. When you take the time to put your needs ahead of everyone else's, you let everyone know that *you* are the priority in your life, and isn't that the way it should be?

Making your needs a priority may be difficult at first, but I want to encourage you to stay firm. In the beginning, your family and co-workers are going to meet this new line of thought with some resistance, but after some time they'll begin to see that in giving yourself the time you need, you're able to give them a better version of yourself.

In order to bring solitude into your daily life, follow what I call the *5 Steps to Solitude.*

1. **Schedule time for yourself -** If you have to, schedule time for yourself by writing it on your calendar and then post your schedule where everyone is sure to see it. Adjust the schedule of everyone else if you need to. Give your quiet time a name. By giving it a name, you'll be more inclined to include it in your day. Perhaps you want to call it your "Me Time" or your "Power Hour."

2. **Shut off all electronics -** Silence your television, your cell phone, and your computer.

3. **Sit still -** Be still and meditate. A still body allows for a still mind. Focus on your breathing with slow deep breaths. Many of the answers we are seeking come to us during the stillness. Allowing yourself even a few minutes of stillness will help you feel refreshed.

4. **Start off small -** In the beginning, you might find it difficult to steal even a few minutes for yourself, so start small. Start by taking just five minutes a day. Over time, you can increase your time to fit your needs.

5. **Say NO -** Learn to say NO. Don't worry about offending someone or disappointing them. Instead learn to say, "I would love to help but I already have too much on my plate right now to take on anything else."

Once you've mastered the *5 Steps to Solitude*, you'll begin to see a huge difference in yourself.

What can I do during my free time?

When you take time for yourself, make sure you're engaged in something that is meaningful to you. You might want to make time to exercise, to enjoy a stroll on the beach, a yoga session, or even a hike through the woods. You might want to enroll in a creative class or treat yourself to a day of shopping, the spa, or lunch with your friends.

Try taking a few minutes every day to meditate. Even if you aren't in the habit of meditating on a daily basis, you will soon discover that even a few minutes of daily quiet time will work wonders to improve both your body and your mind. Not only will you begin to appreciate having less chatter in your mind, but you will also feel more energized.

Whenever you make time for yourself, the most important thing you'll want to remember is to make sure you are spending this valuable time in the present moment. Time is the one gift you can't get back, so learn to appreciate every moment. It is only by living in the moment that we can begin to feel fulfilled and at peace with ourselves.

What are the benefits of taking time for self-care?

Listening to the needs of your body and taking mindful breaks lets your mind, body, and soul know that their well-being matters. In time, you will feel more productive, more energized, and even more creative because your needs are being met.

Taking time to care for yourself will also help to reduce some of the stress in your life. Even though the same stress factors may be present in your life, your reactions to these stress factors will be different because you will feel more at peace with yourself. This can lower your blood pressure, aid in healing, and improve your general well-being.

Take Time for Self-Care

Your soul needs time for solitude and self-reflection.
In order to love, lead, heal, and create, you must nourish yourself first.

-ANONYMOUS

How do you take time to feed your soul? Write a list of all the activities you can do to keep your soul happy. Choose one activity to complete today and write about your experience.

_____

_____

_____

_____

_____

_____

_____

_____

_____

_____

_____

_____

_____

_____

_____

_____

_____

_____

Notes

Morning Routine

You will never change your life until you change something you do daily.
The secret of your success is found in your daily routine.

-John C. Maxwell

Morning Routine

Your first ritual that you do during the day is the highest leveraged ritual, by far, because it has the effect of setting your mind and setting the context for the rest of your day.

-Eben Pagan

Everyone's morning routine is different. For some of us, our morning routine may consist of getting up an hour or so earlier than the rest of the household in order to enjoy a few moments of solitude. We might use this time to practice yoga or meditation, to journal, or to read a few inspirational pages before beginning our day. For others, our morning routine may consist of hitting the snooze button a few extra times before finally getting ourselves out of bed and reaching for that much needed cup of mojo.

Why should you implement a morning routine?

How you begin your morning plays a huge role in how the rest of your day will play out. Studies have shown that people who choose to begin their morning with a positive and uplifting routine are happier and more successful in life than others.

How do you implement a morning routine?

If the concept of a morning routine is something new for you, you'll want to start out slowly, making one small change at a time. Many experts believe that it takes a period of at least twenty-one days to successfully implement a new habit.

For example, if you want to wake up earlier but find you're repeatedly hitting that snooze button, make a commitment that starting tomorrow you are going to get up and out of bed (that's important) the moment the alarm sounds. If you have to set several alarms in several different rooms in order to force yourself out of bed, then do so. When you've mastered the task of getting up (and out of bed) on time, then you can slowly begin to add new rituals into your morning routine.

Be patient with yourself whenever you begin a new routine. Take the time to celebrate each small victory you make along the way. By taking the time to acknowledge even the smallest of steps, you'll up your chances for success and be more encouraged to keep working toward your new habit.

What should your morning routine consist of?

What you decide to add into your morning routine is entirely up to you. What one person deems important enough to include in a morning routine may not have any importance to another individual. Your morning ritual should revolve around your needs and your schedule. Remember, the main purpose in having a structured morning routine is so you can begin your day on a positive note. So ask yourself: *Which activities are important enough to me that I'll be willing to get up early for every day?*

Your next step will be to decide how much time you want to spend on each of the activities you have chosen. If this is your first time following a structured routine, I would suggest starting with small increments of times. Five minutes for each activity is usually a good starting point. Another suggestion would be to keep your entire morning routine to under an hour. By keeping your allotted time for each activity short, you'll be more successful and more apt to follow through the next day. As you become more grounded, you can increase the amount of time you spend on each activity.

Next, you'll want to record your schedule. You might even consider having a different schedule for the days that you are at work and another for the days that you are off. The important thing to remember is that your morning schedule needs to fit your lifestyle and your personal goals, whatever that may be. If you're not already a morning person, creating a morning routine that fits your lifestyle may be exactly what you need to do to insure that your day begins on a positive note.

Here are some suggestions that I have found to be helpful when implementing a morning routine:

- **Create a schedule and stick to it** - Post your schedule in a prominent place and refer to it daily. You might want to consider creating a habit tracking chart to cross off each activity as you complete it. Installing a habit tracking app on your phone can be another way to chart your progress. Find something that will work for you so that you can stay vested in your new routine.

- **Set a timer** - Setting a timer for yourself will make it easier for you to stick to your allotted times. As you get more comfortable with the routine, you can adjust your times as needed.

- **Refrain from screen time** - Turn off your phone, computer and television; turning on any of these devises will only distract you from completing your new routine.

- **Evaluate your routine often and adjust it accordingly** - Be willing to add some new rituals to your routine as you go along. Doing this will keep your routine meaningful.

- **Hydrate yourself** - Having a cup of warm lemon water not only provides your body with the hydration it needs after a night of rest, but the antioxidants will also help to kick start your body in many amazing ways. Drinking a glass of water first thing in the morning will aid digestion, stimulate your organs, and give your skin a healthy glow.

- **Brush your teeth and wash your face right away** - It's a great way to jumpstart your day.

- **Plan ahead** - Your morning routine will be a lot easier if you can prep for some of your morning tasks the night before. By planning ahead, you might find a few extra minutes to devote to your new morning routine.

My mornings always begin with a cup of warm lemon water or a cup of herbal tea. While enjoying my morning drink, I like to spend a few minutes reading from my three favorite morning books:

- *Simple Abundance: A Daybook of Comfort and Joy* by Sarah Ban Breathnach
- *Journey to the Heart- Daily Meditations on the Path to Freeing Your Soul* by Melody Beattie
- *Finding the Gift - Daily Meditations for Mindfulness* by Angela Howell

My morning reads are always instrumental in helping me set a positive tone for the day. I'm always amazed at how much the material I'm reading in one book aligns with what I'm reading in another book. I also enjoy reading personal development books because I am always trying to create a better version of myself. You can check out some of my favorite personal development books at the end of this book.

After my morning reads, I journal for about fifteen minutes. Some days, the material from my morning reads becomes the inspiration for that day's journaling. At other times, I enjoy writing in a prompted journal. Two of my favorite prompted journals are the *Be Inspired Journal* and *The Mindfulness Journal*. Find one that speaks to you and start writing.

After I read and journal, I use the next fifteen to twenty minutes to meditate as I find this is the best time for me to consciously absorb the information I have just read. One of my favorite meditation apps is *Insight Timer*. I also enjoy listening to Jason Stephenson and davidgi, as I find both of these men to be extremely inspirational.

Following my quiet time, I complete my affirmations. Some days I may choose to write my affirmations in my journal. At other times, I may choose to read affirmations from one of my favorite sites and repeat them aloud (repeating them in front of a mirror is highly effective), or at other times I may choose to listen to a guided affirmation meditation. I especially enjoy listening to the *Think Yourself Slim Morning Gratitude Positive Affirmations*. Afterwards, I set my intentions for the day and then take a few more minutes to visualize exactly how I want my day to play out.

I also make sure I find time to exercise. My husband and I visit our local gym three times a week. On the days I don't visit the gym, I make time to walk. When I first began this book, I was living in the beautiful coastal town of Cape May, New Jersey and I would often walk the beach in the morning looking for sea glass and seashells. I have since moved to a coastal town in South Carolina where the beaches are plentiful, the weather is warmer, and the taxes are lower.

What are the benefits of establishing a morning routine?

Creating a morning routine that works for you will take time, but soon you'll come to appreciate the positive changes in yourself. You'll feel more productive and have more energy. You may also feel more grounded, and less stressed throughout the day. When you commit to a morning routine, you'll feel happier, healthier, and ultimately, more at peace because you've taken the time to connect with your inner self.

Morning Routine

Your day is pretty much formed by how you spend your first hour.
Check your thoughts, attitude, and heart.

-Anonymous

Describe your typical morning routine from the moment you first wake up until your actual day begins. Are there any changes you can make in your morning routine that will allow you to enjoy a more positive day?

_____

_____

_____

_____

_____

_____

_____

_____

_____

_____

_____

_____

_____

_____

_____

_____

_____

_____

_____

_____

Notes

Journaling

Journaling is like whispering to one's self and listening at the same time.

-Mina Murray, Dracula

Journaling

Each time you make an entry into your journal, you open another door into yourself.

-Lucia Capacchione, The Well-Being Journal

The word *journal* is derived from the Old French word *jurnal,* meaning a day's work; and the Latin word, *diurnalis,* meaning daily. Merriam Webster defines a journal as a record of experiences, ideas, or reflections kept regularly for private use. To me, journaling is a way of talking to yourself and then listening to what you've said in order to create a better version of yourself.

Why should you keep a journal?

A journal is a bridge to self-discovery, a tool that you can use to help identify your strengths and your weaknesses; it is a place where you can record your triumphs along with your disappointments. Through journaling, we gain the opportunity to connect with our inner self while clarifying our thoughts.

Julia Cameron, author of *The Artist's Way,* suggests writing three pages every morning. She calls these *morning pages* and suggests that you write about anything, everything, or nothing. On those days when you feel you don't have anything to write about, simply fill up your three pages by just writing whatever thoughts come to your mind, even if those thoughts consist of nothing else other than *I don't have anything to write about.* Chances are good that somewhere within those three pages, you'll find something else to write about. It doesn't really matter what you write about as long as you are writing.

"Morning pages are nonnegotiable," says Julia. "Morning pages are the primary tool of creative recovery." "Morning pages do get us to the other side: the other side of our fear, of our negativity, of our moods." "Morning pages," Julia goes on to say, "will teach you to stop judging yourself. So what if you're tired, crabby, distracted, stressed? Your artist is a child and it needs to be fed. Morning pages feed your artist child. So write your morning pages."

Morning pages, in my opinion, are a great way to begin the day because you're choosing to begin the day by being honest with yourself. In doing so, you'll gain a better understanding of yourself and appreciate yourself for who you truly are. Journaling will also help you to feel grounded. This will inspire you to find the creativity that lies within you; to help you find your artist child. In fact, it was only a few months after I began my morning pages that I was inspired to create the journal you are now reading.

Over time, I've come to find that the days I begin with journaling are somewhat easier for me to manage. Journaling, for me, is a safe haven where I can record my most private thoughts, my worries, and my wildest hopes and dreams without fear of being judged by others. Within the pages of my journal, I feel safe to write about the truths I'm afraid to speak aloud. In writing about these truths, I've come to accept them for what they are, and to grow from what I've learned about myself.

Journaling can also be a positive way to deal with the stress in life. Let's face it, we all have stressful days. Stress will always be a constant in life; a constant that we cannot control. The only thing we can control is how we choose to react to it.

When I choose to respond to the stress in my life through writing, it provides me with a quieter alternative than if I were to act out physically or verbally. Through writing, I'm able to release some of the tension associated from that stress. Although the events and stress of the day may still be the same, my reactions to these situations will have changed and thus I am better able to respond to them. On my most difficult days, my journal is often the anchor that helps me stay afloat.

What I love most about journaling is that there are so many ways to journal; there are gratitude journals, bullet journals, prompted journals, poetry journals, online journals, and traditional journals. There is no wrong way to journal so find a style that speaks to you and just start writing. Don't worry about what to write in your journal—simply listen to what your heart has to say and your words will soon fill up the pages of your journal.

What are the benefits of keeping a journal?

Journaling is a wonderful way to ignite the creativity that lies within all of us. It's also a great way to improve your vocabulary skills and writing skills. When we journal, we create a connection between mindfulness and happiness. We become more compassionate, empathetic, and less judgmental.

Journaling

Either write something worth reading or do something worth writing.

-BEN FRANKLIN

Journaling on a daily basis opens the gateway to creativity. Do you enjoy keeping a gratitude journal, a bullet journal, or some other type of journal? Do you enjoy writing stories or poetry? Describe the type of writing you most enjoy.

_____

_____

_____

_____

_____

_____

_____

_____

_____

_____

_____

_____

_____

_____

_____

_____

_____

_____

_____

_____

Notes

Setting Goals

A dream written down with a date becomes a goal. A goal broken down into steps becomes a plan. A plan backed by action makes your dreams come true.

-GREG REID

Setting Goals

A goal is a dream with a deadline.

-Napoleon Hill

If you want to be successful and accomplish great things in life, it's crucial to set goals that will help manifest your desires. Creating a detailed action plan can motivate you to remain focused on the goals you want to achieve.

What are some successful strategies for creating a goal?

When I was an elementary teacher, I would often use the bulletin boards in my classroom to motivate my students. One of my favorite bulletin boards read *Motivation Gets Us Started. Habits Keep Us Going.* If you really want to be successful in achieving your goals, it's important to have a foundation of strong habits that will keep you working toward your goal.

One of the best strategies I have ever come across when setting a new goal is the S.M.A.R.T. plan, which stands for: specific, measurable, attainable, relevant, and timely. I would often use this strategy with my students at the beginning of every semester.

Specific	When writing your goal, be specific in what, why, and how you want to achieve your goal. • *By (insert date), I will (state goal) by (provide detailed steps outlining how you plan to achieve those goals).* • *Example: In 2 months, I will have deposited $1000.00 into my European vacation fund by deducting $250.00 from each weekly paycheck.*
Measurable	When creating a goal, it's important to break your goal into manageable steps. Doing so will serve several purposes: 1. It's easier to remain focused on your long-term goal when the steps are broken down into smaller and more manageable steps. 2. Each successful step will provide you with the encouragement to move forward. 3. Smaller steps make it easier for you to track your progress. Remember, the journey of a thousand miles began with a single step, so acknowledge each and every successful step along the way.
Attainable	Is it possible for you to attain your desired goal with the resources, abilities, skills, and knowledge you now possess? If your goal isn't something you feel you can achieve right now, then perhaps you'll want to break your goal into smaller steps and work your way up. It's important to create goals that are within your range. You don't want to set a goal that is unobtainable because it will only create frustration in your life. However, never be afraid to dream big, even if you need to take smaller steps to get there.
Relevant	Is your goal realistic and relevant? Is it reasonable? Ask yourself these questions: • *What do I want to achieve?* • *Why is this goal important to me?*
Timely	When you write out your goals, create a timeframe you can adhere to. Adding a deadline to your goal will keep your focused, but remember to be flexible. If your original timeframe isn't working, don't be afraid to revise it. *When* you achieve your goal shouldn't be as important *as actually achieving it.*

In order to set a S.M.A.R.T. goal that works for you, the first thing you'll need to do is to decide where you most want to see an improvement in your life. Is it your career or your finances that you want to improve? Perhaps you want to make a career change or start saving now for your retirement days. Or maybe you want to become more spiritual, eat healthier, or become more fit?

As you journey through this book, you will have the opportunity to create a goal every thirty days. I have included two goal-setting templates for your convenience. Complete whichever template works best for you.

Spend a few minutes of quiet time today and ask yourself: *What are my dreams? What do I need to do to make my dreams happen?* Be patient with yourself as you wait for the answers to come. Listen to your heart; your heart will guide you in the right direction.

Once you have an answer, create a plan and put it into action. Start believing that the Universe is going to do everything in its Power to help turn your dream into a reality. As long as you believe in the magic of dreams and you're willing to work hard to make it happen, it will happen.

What are the benefits of setting goals?

John Dewey, an American philosopher, psychologist, and educational reformer once said, "Arriving at one goal is the starting point to another." When you achieve a goal that you've worked hard to accomplish, it will provide you with a sense of personal satisfaction and pride, and it will also encourage you to put new desires into action. When you manifest the goals that you have set for yourself, you create a better version of yourself which is something we should all be striving for.

When it comes to setting goals, C.S. Lewis reminds us that "We are never too old to set another goal or to dream a new dream."

Setting Goals

If you set goals and go after them with all the determination you can muster,
your gifts will take you places that will amaze you.

-LES BROWN

Are you a goal-oriented person? Do you feel it's important to set goals? Why or why not?

_____

_____

_____

_____

_____

_____

_____

_____

_____

_____

_____

_____

_____

_____

_____

_____

_____

_____

_____

_____

_____

Notes

Visualization

What you think, you become. What you feel, you attract. What you imagine, you create.

-BUDDHA

Visualization

Imagination is everything. It is the preview of life's coming attractions.

-ALBERT EINSTEIN

Scientists are just now beginning to understand the true power of visualization and believe it to be the most underrated and underutilized part of the mind. According to Shakti Gawain, author of *Creative Visualization*, "Creative visualization is the act of using mental images and affirmations to produce positive changes in your life."

Visualization really does have the power to change your life. In fact, many successful people and celebrities alike credit their success to visualization. For now, though, let's take a look at some of the people who credit their success to visualization and hear what they have to say about the topic.

Jim Carrey - Comedian/Actor - When Canadian comic Jim Carrey was just beginning his career, somewhere around 1985, he decided to drive his beat-up Toyota to Los Angeles to chance his talent. Once there, he stopped to look at his new surroundings. Wanting to visualize his success, he wrote himself a check in the amount of $10 million dollars, dated the check ten years into the future, and placed the check in his wallet. Ten years later, Jim was offered a role in the movie "Dumb and Dumber" to the tune of ten million dollars! When his dad passed away in 1994, Jim placed the check in his dad's casket as a thank you for the support he had shown him throughout the years. Jim is a firm believer in the Law of Attraction and continues to speak publicly about its power.

Tug McGraw - Major League Baseball relief pitcher and father of Tim McGraw, country singer and actor - Tug grew up loving baseball and eventually played with the New York Mets and the Philadelphia Phillies. Tug is best known for coining the phrase "You Gotta Believe" which went out to become a popular rally cry used by the New York Mets. In 1980, while playing for the Philadelphia Phillies in the World Series, Tug's "You Gotta Believe" attitude and his practice of visualization helped him to strike out Willie Wilson of the Kansas City Royals and win the World Series. When asked about that day, Tug had this to say about that game: "It was as if I'd been there a 1000 times before. When I was growing up, I would pitch to my father in the backyard. We would always get to where it was the bottom of the ninth with two outs and three men at base. I would always bear down and strike them out." He went on to say, "Kids should practice autographing baseballs. This is a skill they overlook in Little League."

John Assaraf - Brain researcher/entrepreneur - John believes strongly in the power of visualization and often creates vision boards to help manifest his goals. Shortly after moving into his new home, his son who was five years old at the time, walked into John's office and asked his father what was inside the stack of boxes that were on the floor. John explained that they were his vision boards. Not knowing what a vision board was, John took out one of his vision boards that he had created several years earlier to share with his son. On the vision board John had pasted a picture of a 7,000 square foot home he hoped to own someday. Also included on this spacious six acre property was a guest house, an office complex and an orange tree grove. When John took this vision board out of the box, he cried. The house on his vision board was the same home that John and his family had just moved into!

Cherie Carter Scott - New York Times bestselling author of personal development books, and life coach - Cherie Carter-Scott is considered to be the pioneer of the life coaching industry and is often referred to as The Mother of Coaching. Carter-Scott has said, "Ordinary people believe only in the possible. Extraordinary people visualize not what is possible or probable, but rather what is impossible. And by visualizing the impossible, they begin to see it as possible."

Andrew Carnegie - Industrialist/Philanthropist - Carnegie, one of the most influential people during the American industrial revolution, went on to become one of the wealthiest people in America, with a net value of $310 billion. "I am no longer cursed by poverty because I took possession of my own mind and that mind has yielded me every material that I want, and much more than I need. But the power of mind is a universal one, available to the humblest person as it is to the greatest," said Carnegie of the power of visualization.

Creative visualization is a powerful motivational tool available to all of us at absolutely no cost. When you make the decision to visualize exactly what it is you want and choose to believe it's already yours, it becomes easier to manifest what you most desire. Visualization puts the magic into our dreams; allowing our dreams of today to become our realities of tomorrow.

So if visualization is really as simple as imagining what you want and believing you already have it, why then do so few of us engage in this activity? The answer is that many of us simply don't know how to use visualization to its fullest potential.

In order to learn why visualization works, let's take a closer look inside our mind to understand how it works. Later, within this section, I'll share with you the steps you'll need to take so that you, too, can learn how to visualize and materialize your desires.

How does visualization work?

Everything in our world is comprised of energy and that energy vibrates at different speeds depending on its frequency. The lighter something is, the less energy it carries and the easier it is to move or change.

Energy is attracted to other energies having a similar frequency, just like a magnet is attracted to another magnet. Inside our brain there are billions of neurons connected to one another. The neurons in your brain carry electrical impulses and are always looking to attach themselves to other neurons having a similar charge, so to speak. They act like a human transmitter, always on the lookout for a *like* signal to connect to. This concept of like attracts like is called the *Law of Attraction*.

Even our thoughts are created from energy. In following with the Law of Attraction, our thoughts are always looking for thoughts having a similar energy. This is why there is so much truth in the idea that positive thinking people attract more positive energies into their lives while negative thinking people attract more negative energies.

When a thought is first conceived, whether negative or positive, the neurons in your brain begin searching to connect with other neurons having a similar energy. As these neurons grow in number so does their strength. This collected group of neurons will now work together to create a mental image of your thought. Once that mental image is in place, the neurons join forces to change your thought into form. They want your thoughts to now perform, so to speak. In essence, visualization is like a dress rehearsal of the mind. This is the Law of Attraction working at its finest.

Everything that has ever been invented was first the thought of the inventor before it took form. This is exactly why so many quantum scientists believe that our entire universe is a creation of thought that has eventually taken shape.

Why should one adopt a practice of visualization?

Whether you believe it in or not, visualization is always at work and you are already using it on a daily basis. When you're hungry, you imagine the meal you want to eat. When you're tired, you imagine your head hitting the pillow on your bed. Or perhaps you're thinking of a particular friend when suddenly you receive a phone call or a visit from them. These are just a few example of visualization at work.

In his book *Peak Performance*, author Charles Garfield talks about a mental training study that was conducted by a team of scientists in Russia. Knowing that the brain stimulates the body to perform what it sees mentally, this team of scientists conducted a study with their athletes who were training for the 1980 Olympics to see whether or not the body really can achieve what the mind believes. To test this theory, they divided their athletes into four different groups that would train in the following manner:

- Group 1 trained with 100% physical training
- Group 2 trained with 75% physical training and 25% mental training
- Group 3 trained with 50% physical training and 50% mental training and
- Group 4 trained with 25% physical training and 75% mental training.

At the conclusion of this study, it was determined that the group of athletes who trained mostly with their mind outperformed those athletes who had received more physical training.

If visualization can work for all of the celebrities we mentioned earlier in this section and it has been proven to work for athletes, it can work for you too! Now, you just need to learn how to use it to your highest good so that you, too, can manifest all you desire.

Before visualization can work for you, *"You Gotta Believe."* If you believe in yourself and you're willing to work for what you want, the Universe will work along with you to manifest your dreams. The only things that will prevent you from getting what you want out of life are your self-doubts and fears. Don't let either of these keep you from pursuing what you most desire.

The other thing you need to do in order to get visualization to work is to practice it often. When you start using visualization on a steady basis, your subconscious will start to view this new line of thinking as a pattern and will work harder to repeat this pattern.

Your thoughts really do create your life. That's why there is so much merit in the adage: *Change your thoughts, change your life.* If you really want to change your life, then you need to change your thinking. It's up to you, and only you, to make the changes you want to happen in your life.

What steps should you take to start visualizing?

Visualization takes practice. In order to manifest your dreams, you need to work hard to make it happen. Make a commitment that you will do whatever it takes to obtain your goal. Remember, the Universe isn't going to wave a magic wand and drop something in your lap if you are not working to your greatest potential.

1. **Relax** - Before you ask for anything, it's important to be relaxed. If you're tensed and stressed out, you'll confuse the Universe and it may present you with something that you didn't ask for. So sit or lie down in a comfortable position. You can choose to keep your eyes open or closed, whichever feels more comfortable for you. Now, take a long inhale breath, hold for three seconds, and exhale slowly and fully. Do this several times until your heart rate slows down and you feel a sense of calmness.

2. **Set your goal** - What exactly is it that you want? Do you want to shed a few pounds, become more fit, or become more connected in a spiritual way? Or is it a new job, relationship, or home that you want?

3. **Be specific** - When creating the mental image of what you desire, be as specific as you can in your request. If it's a new car that you want, include the color, make, model, and the price you want to pay for the car and when you want to receive the car. Use as many sensory details as possible to help you visualize exactly what you want.

4. **Assume what you want has already been manifested** - Imagine that whatever it is you're asking for has already been fulfilled. It's important to always remain in the present tense when thinking about what you want because if you imagine your vision in the future sense, that's exactly where it will stay, in the future and unobtainable.

5. **Stay focused on your goal** - Visualize your goal often. The more energy you put into your visualization, the sooner you will obtain it. Instead of focusing on what can go wrong, stay focused on what can go right and then wait for it to happen.
    A great technique for remaining focused on your goal is to create a vision board. A vision board (or a vision map) is a tool that contains images of the goal you want to manifest along with the steps you'll need to take in order to achieve the goal. You can cut pictures out of magazines or draw them yourself.

Once your vision board is complete, keep it in a prominent place where you can refer to it often. You might want to hang your vision board on your bulletin board or your refrigerator, tape it on your mirror, tack it on your ceiling, or use it as a screen saver. The important thing is to keep the vision board in a place where you will see it often so that it will continue to keep you focused on your goal. A vision board, in my opinion, is the North Star of your dreams, always guiding you on the path you need to take.

I believe in the magic of vision boards so much that I've incorporated them into this journal. During the course of your journey in this journal, you'll have several opportunities to create vision boards to help you manifest your dreams.

6. **Allow for bigger possibilities** - It's always a good idea to add a statement that will allude to something more than what you originally asked for. If you add the words *or something even better,* then you are leaving the door open for even bigger possibilities to come your way.

7. **Re-evaluate your vision** - Is there anything you need to change, add, or edit to your original request? Always keep your mind open to new solutions, new opportunities, or new possibilities that may come your way. Adjust for any changes that you might want. Continue to focus on exactly what it is that you want; the more your subconscious hears what it is that you want, the harder it will work to manifest your goal.

Know, too, that some things may take longer than others before they manifest. Be patient while the Universe takes care of granting what you want. While you're waiting, give yourself a pep talk. Offer yourself encouraging words along the way such as: *I know the Universe is working its magic to bring me what I want.*

8. **Give 100% effort** - Don't concern yourself with how things will happen; the Universe will take care of that for you. The only thing you need to do is to stay committed to your goal and to do whatever it takes to turn your dreams of today into tomorrow's reality.

What are the benefits of visualization?

We know how powerful visualization can be in helping us to achieve our desires, but visualization can also benefit the mind, body, and soul in some amazing ways. Visualizing allows your mind to produce more alpha waves, which can help to heal the body by reducing stress, decreasing pain, and lowering your blood pressure.

Visualization

Visualize this thing that you want. See it, feel it, believe in it.
Make your mental blue print, and begin to build.

-ROBERT COLLIER

What is it that you most want out of life? In your mind, visualize exactly what you want. Draw a picture of the image you have in your mind, remembering to add as many details as possible.

Notes

PART
three

Every great dream begins with a dreamer.
Always remember, you have within you the strength, the patience,
and the passion to reach for the stars to change the world.

-Harriet Tubman

You are about to embark on
a journey of self-discovery.

Let's get started.

I am...

These two words, used together, have the ability to transform your life.

Depending on the words that follow, the statement *I am* can make a huge difference in how we view ourselves. We become what we believe ourselves to be. So, if we grew up always hearing negative *I am* statements, we begin to believe what we've heard and we become that person. On the contrary, if we grew up always hearing positive *I am* statements, then we, in turn, grow up with a more positive self-image.

Our thoughts are powerful and can transform our life. When we make a conscious effort to change how we view ourselves, we can create an even better version of ourselves.

Your task for today is to complete the **I AM** sentence on the opposite page in as many positive ways as you possibly can. You may want to complete the sentence by using single words; such as *I am beautiful, I am smart, I am trustworthy.* You may want to complete the sentence by using words that define your roles in life; *I am a loving mother, a devoted wife, a teacher, a sister, etc.* Or perhaps you want to complete the sentence by using a phrase or an affirmation such *as I am developing healthy eating habits and exercising every day; I am open to the abundance the Universe has in store for me; I am the creator of my own destiny.*

How you choose to complete the worksheet is entirely up to you. Remember, this is your journal so personalize it to fit your needs.

Once you have completed the page, make several copies to post in a prominent place and refer to this page often during your day. Repeat your **I AM** statements often throughout the day. The more you say it, and the more you believe it, the sooner you will become it.

Bo Bennett, a motivational speaker and author, once said, "A dream becomes a goal when action is taken toward its achievement." If you want your dreams to happen, you need to take action.

What goals do you have for your life? What are your goals for this week, this month, this year, a year from now, or even five years from now?

Remember, you alone are the creator of your life. If you are serious about turning your dreams into a reality, you need to put a plan into action… NOW!

Decide what it is you want to focus on and then outline the steps you'll need to take in order to turn your dreams into your reality. On the next two pages, you'll find two goal-setting worksheets.

Choose the worksheet that works best for you to outline your plan. Once you have a plan in place, you'll use it to create a vision board to help you manifest your dreams.

It's your time
to dream.

Dream big!

My **GOAL-SETTING** Worksheet

Today's Date _____ **Goal Completion Date** _____

My goal is (be as specific as you can): _____
_____
_____

These are the steps I will need to take in order to achieve my goal:

1. _____
2. _____
3. _____
4. _____

When I am discouraged, I will remind myself why it's important to achieve this goal.

I want to achieve this goal because_____
_____
_____

I will track my progress here _____
_____
_____

When I achieve my goal, I will _____
_____
_____

S.M.A.R.T. GOALS *Worksheet*

Specific	What exactly do you want to accomplish?
Measurable	How will you track your progress?
Attainable	Do you have the skills and resources to attain this goal? What steps do you need to take to achieve your goal?
Relevant	Why is this goal important to you?
Timely	When do you want to complete this goal?

Create Your **Vision Board**

Now that you have identified your goal for this month and you've outlined the steps you need to take to reach your goal, let's have some fun and create a vision board that will keep you motivated.

Feel free to use the blank box on the next page to practice your design. You can then use the next two pages to create your vision board for the goal you have selected for this month.

Feel free to add photographs, quotes, and anything else that will help you to remain focused on achieving your goal.

Have fun!

VISION

BOARD

Life is either a daring adventure or nothing at all.
—Helen Keller

Reflection

Describe one of your greatest adventures in life.

_____
_____
_____
_____
_____
_____
_____
_____
_____
_____
_____
_____
_____
_____
_____
_____
_____

Intention

What is your intention for today? Just for today...

_____
_____
_____

Meditation

How long did you meditate today? What type of meditation did you
complete? Journal about today's meditation experience.

_____
_____
_____

Gratitude

Which three things are you grateful for today?

_____

_____

Reading

Write one thought from today's reading that was meaningful to you.

_____

_____

Exercise

Record how you chose to exercise today.

_____

_____

Affirmations

Write three affirmations for today.

_____

_____

Time for Self-Care

Reflect on what you did today to nourish your soul.

_____

_____

How would you rate today?

1   2   3   4   5   6   7   8   9   10

If you want to fly, give up everything that weighs you down.
-Anonymous

Reflection

What do you need to let go of in order to fly?

_____

_____

_____

_____

_____

_____

_____

_____

_____

_____

_____

_____

_____

Intention

What is your intention for today? Just for today...

_____

_____

Meditation

How long did you meditate today? What type of meditation did you complete? Journal about today's meditation experience.

_____

_____

_____

Gratitude

Which three things are you grateful for today?

_____

_____

_____

Reading

Write one thought from today's reading that was meaningful to you.

_____

_____

_____

Exercise

Record how you chose to exercise today.

_____

_____

_____

Affirmations

Write three affirmations for today.

_____

_____

_____

Time for Self-Care

Reflect on what you did today to nourish your soul.

_____

_____

_____

How would you rate today?

1   2   3   4   5   6   7   8   9   10

Do something today that your future self will thank you for.
-Anonymous

Reflection

What can you do today that your future self will thank you for?

_____
_____
_____
_____
_____
_____
_____
_____
_____
_____
_____
_____
_____
_____

Intention

What is your intention for today? Just for today...

_____
_____
_____

Meditation

How long did you meditate today? What type of meditation did you complete? Journal about today's meditation experience.

_____
_____
_____

Gratitude

Which three things are you grateful for today?

_____

_____

_____

Reading

Write one thought from today's reading that was meaningful to you.

_____

_____

_____

Exercise

Record how you chose to exercise today.

_____

_____

_____

Affirmations

Write three affirmations for today.

_____

_____

_____

Time for Self-Care

Reflect on what you did today to nourish your soul.

_____

_____

_____

How would you rate today?

1   2   3   4   5   6   7   8   9   10

The struggle you're in today is developing the strength for tomorrow.

-Robert Tew

Reflection

Describe how your struggles have shaped you into the person you are today.

_____

_____

_____

_____

_____

_____

_____

_____

_____

_____

_____

_____

_____

_____

_____

Intention

What is your intention for today? Just for today...

_____

_____

Meditation

How long did you meditate today? What type of meditation did you complete? Journal about today's meditation experience.

_____

_____

_____

Gratitude

Which three things are you grateful for today?

_____

_____

_____

Reading

Write one thought from today's reading that was meaningful to you.

_____

_____

_____

Exercise

Record how you chose to exercise today.

_____

_____

_____

Affirmations

Write three affirmations for today.

_____

_____

_____

Time for Self-Care

Reflect on what you did today to nourish your soul.

_____

_____

_____

How would you rate today?   1   2   3   4   5   6   7   8   9   10

Sometimes your only available transportation is a leap of faith
-Margaret Shepard

Reflection

Describe a time when faith guided your path.

_____
_____
_____
_____
_____
_____
_____
_____
_____
_____
_____
_____
_____
_____
_____
_____
_____

Intention

What is your intention for today? Just for today...

_____
_____
_____

Meditation

How long did you meditate today? What type of meditation did you complete? Journal about today's meditation experience.

_____
_____
_____

Gratitude

Which three things are you grateful for today?

_____

_____

_____

Reading

Write one thought from today's reading that was meaningful to you.

_____

_____

_____

Exercise

Record how you chose to exercise today.

_____

_____

_____

Affirmations

Write three affirmations for today.

_____

_____

_____

Time for Self-Care

Reflect on what you did today to nourish your soul.

_____

_____

_____

How would you rate today?   1   2   3   4   5   6   7   8   9   10

You must be the change you want to see in the world.
-Mahatma Gandhi

Reflection

Describe one change that you would like to see in the world. What will you need to do to make this change possible?

_____
_____
_____
_____
_____
_____
_____
_____
_____
_____
_____
_____
_____
_____
_____

Intention

What is your intention for today? Just for today...

_____
_____

Meditation

How long did you meditate today? What type of meditation did you complete? Journal about today's meditation experience.

_____
_____
_____

Gratitude

Which three things are you grateful for today?

_____

_____

_____

Reading

Write one thought from today's reading that was meaningful to you.

_____

_____

_____

Exercise

Record how you chose to exercise today.

_____

_____

_____

Affirmations

Write three affirmations for today.

_____

_____

_____

Time for Self-Care

Reflect on what you did today to nourish your soul.

_____

_____

_____

How would you rate today?   1   2   3   4   5   6   7   8   9   10

You never fail until you stop trying.
-Albert Einstein

Reflection

Write about something that you will never stop trying to achieve.

_____

_____

_____

_____

_____

_____

_____

_____

_____

_____

_____

_____

_____

_____

_____

_____

Intention

What is your intention for today? Just for today...

_____

_____

Meditation

How long did you meditate today? What type of meditation did you complete? Journal about today's meditation experience.

_____

_____

_____

Gratitude
Which three things are you grateful for today?

_____

_____

_____

Reading
Write one thought from today's reading that was meaningful to you.

_____

_____

_____

Exercise
Record how you chose to exercise today.

_____

_____

_____

Affirmations
Write three affirmations for today.

_____

_____

_____

Time for Self-Care
Reflect on what you did today to nourish your soul.

_____

_____

_____

How would you rate today?   1   2   3   4   5   6   7   8   9   10

The meaning of life is to find your gift. The purpose of life is to give it away.

-William Shakespeare

Reflection

What is your gift in life? How can you share your gift with others?

_____

_____

_____

_____

_____

_____

_____

_____

_____

_____

_____

_____

_____

_____

_____

Intention

What is your intention for today? Just for today...

_____

_____

Meditation

How long did you meditate today? What type of meditation did you complete? Journal about today's meditation experience.

_____

_____

_____

Gratitude

Which three things are you grateful for today?

_____
_____
_____

Reading

Write one thought from today's reading that was meaningful to you.

_____
_____
_____

Exercise

Record how you chose to exercise today.

_____
_____
_____

Affirmations

Write three affirmations for today.

_____
_____
_____

Time for Self-Care

Reflect on what you did today to nourish your soul.

_____
_____
_____

How would you rate today?

1   2   3   4   5   6   7   8   9   10

Travel is the only thing you can buy that will make you richer.
-Anonymous

Reflection

Describe a place where you have been and explain the riches you gained from this experience.

_____
_____
_____
_____
_____
_____
_____
_____
_____
_____
_____
_____
_____
_____
_____
_____

Intention

What is your intention for today? Just for today...

_____
_____
_____

Meditation

How long did you meditate today? What type of meditation did you complete? Journal about today's meditation experience.

_____
_____
_____

Gratitude

Which three things are you grateful for today?

_____

_____

_____

Reading

Write one thought from today's reading that was meaningful to you.

_____

_____

_____

Exercise

Record how you chose to exercise today.

_____

_____

_____

Affirmations

Write three affirmations for today.

_____

_____

_____

Time for Self-Care

Reflect on what you did today to nourish your soul.

_____

_____

_____

How would you rate today?

1   2   3   4   5   6   7   8   9   10

Failure is a lesson learned. Success is a lesson applied.
-Anonymous

Reflection

Describe an important lesson you've learned from a failure in your life.

_____

_____

_____

_____

_____

_____

_____

_____

_____

_____

_____

_____

_____

_____

_____

Intention

What is your intention for today? Just for today...

_____

_____

Meditation

How long did you meditate today? What type of meditation did you complete? Journal about today's meditation experience.

_____

_____

_____

Gratitude
Which three things are you grateful for today?

_____

_____

_____

Reading
Write one thought from today's reading that was meaningful to you.

_____

_____

_____

Exercise
Record how you chose to exercise today.

_____

_____

_____

Affirmations
Write three affirmations for today.

_____

_____

_____

Time for Self-Care
Reflect on what you did today to nourish your soul.

_____

_____

_____

How would you rate today?   1   2   3   4   5   6   7   8   9   10

Go confidently in the direction of your dreams. Live the life you've imagined.

-Henry David Thoreau

Reflection

How do you imagine the life of your dreams?

_____

_____

_____

_____

_____

_____

_____

_____

_____

_____

_____

_____

_____

_____

_____

Intention

What is your intention for today? Just for today...

_____

_____

Meditation

How long did you meditate today? What type of meditation did you complete? Journal about today's meditation experience.

_____

_____

Gratitude

Which three things are you grateful for today?

_____

_____

_____

Reading

Write one thought from today's reading that was meaningful to you.

_____

_____

_____

Exercise

Record how you chose to exercise today.

_____

_____

_____

Affirmations

Write three affirmations for today.

_____

_____

_____

Time for Self-Care

Reflect on what you did today to nourish your soul.

_____

_____

_____

How would you rate today?   1   2   3   4   5   6   7   8   9   10

I am not what happened to me. I am what I choose to be.
-C.G. Jung

Reflection

Your past does not define you. Describe the person you want to become.

_____
_____
_____
_____
_____
_____
_____
_____
_____
_____
_____
_____
_____
_____
_____

Intention

What is your intention for today? Just for today...

_____
_____
_____

Meditation

How long did you meditate today? What type of meditation did you complete? Journal about today's meditation experience.

_____
_____
_____

Gratitude

Which three things are you grateful for today?

_____

_____

_____

Reading

Write one thought from today's reading that was meaningful to you.

_____

_____

_____

Exercise

Record how you chose to exercise today.

_____

_____

_____

Affirmations

Write three affirmations for today.

_____

_____

_____

Time for Self-Care

Reflect on what you did today to nourish your soul.

_____

_____

_____

How would you rate today?   1   2   3   4   5   6   7   8   9   10

No act of kindness is ever wasted.
 -Aesop

Reflection

What is the kindest act someone has done for you? Describe an act of kindness you did for someone else.

_____

_____

_____

_____

_____

_____

_____

_____

_____

_____

_____

_____

_____

_____

_____

_____

_____

Intention

What is your intention for today? Just for today...

_____

_____

_____

Meditation

How long did you meditate today? What type of meditation did you complete? Journal about today's meditation experience.

_____

_____

_____

Gratitude

Which three things are you grateful for today?

_____

_____

_____

Reading

Write one thought from today's reading that was meaningful to you.

_____

_____

_____

Exercise

Record how you chose to exercise today.

_____

_____

_____

Affirmations

Write three affirmations for today.

_____

_____

_____

Time for Self-Care

Reflect on what you did today to nourish your soul.

_____

_____

_____

How would you rate today?   1   2   3   4   5   6   7   8   9   10

The best time to plant a tree was twenty years ago. The next best time is now.

-Chinese proverb

Reflection

Is there anything you wish you had done earlier in your life?

_____

_____

_____

_____

_____

_____

_____

_____

_____

_____

_____

_____

_____

_____

Intention

What is your intention for today? Just for today...

_____

_____

Meditation

How long did you meditate today? What type of meditation did you complete? Journal about today's meditation experience.

_____

_____

_____

Gratitude

Which three things are you grateful for today?

_____

_____

_____

Reading

Write one thought from today's reading that was meaningful to you.

_____

_____

_____

Exercise

Record how you chose to exercise today.

_____

_____

_____

Affirmations

Write three affirmations for today.

_____

_____

_____

Time for Self-Care

Reflect on what you did today to nourish your soul.

_____

_____

_____

How would you rate today?

1   2   3   4   5   6   7   8   9   10

Believe in what you want so much that it has no choice but to materialize.

-Karen Salmansohn

Reflection

What is the one thing you want most out of life and why?

_____

_____

_____

_____

_____

_____

_____

_____

_____

_____

_____

_____

_____

_____

_____

Intention

What is your intention for today? Just for today...

_____

_____

Meditation

How long did you meditate today? What type of meditation did you complete? Journal about today's meditation experience.

_____

_____

Gratitude

Which three things are you grateful for today?

_____

_____

_____

Reading

Write one thought from today's reading that was meaningful to you.

_____

_____

_____

Exercise

Record how you chose to exercise today.

_____

_____

_____

Affirmations

Write three affirmations for today.

_____

_____

_____

Time for Self-Care

Reflect on what you did today to nourish your soul.

_____

_____

_____

How would you rate today? 1   2   3   4   5   6   7   8   9   10

Your life does not get better by chance. It gets better by change.
-Anonymous

Reflection

If you had to choose one word to create a positive change in your life, what would that one word be and why?

_____

_____

_____

_____

_____

_____

_____

_____

_____

_____

_____

_____

_____

_____

Intention

What is your intention for today? Just for today...

_____

_____

Meditation

How long did you meditate today? What type of meditation did you complete? Journal about today's meditation experience.

_____

_____

_____

Gratitude

Which three things are you grateful for today?

_____

_____

_____

Reading

Write one thought from today's reading that was meaningful to you.

_____

_____

_____

Exercise

Record how you chose to exercise today.

_____

_____

_____

Affirmations

Write three affirmations for today.

_____

_____

_____

Time for Self-Care

Reflect on what you did today to nourish your soul.

_____

_____

_____

How would you rate today?   1   2   3   4   5   6   7   8   9   10

Twenty years from now you'll be more disappointed in the things that you didn't do than the things that you did do.

-Mark Twain

Reflection

Is there anything that you regret not doing when you had the opportunity to do so?

_____

_____

_____

_____

_____

_____

_____

_____

_____

_____

_____

_____

_____

_____

_____

Intention

What is your intention for today? Just for today...

_____

_____

Meditation

How long did you meditate today? What type of meditation did you complete? Journal about today's meditation experience.

_____

_____

Gratitude

Which three things are you grateful for today?

_____

_____

_____

Reading

Write one thought from today's reading that was meaningful to you.

_____

_____

_____

Exercise

Record how you chose to exercise today.

_____

_____

_____

Affirmations

Write three affirmations for today.

_____

_____

_____

Time for Self-Care

Reflect on what you did today to nourish your soul.

_____

_____

_____

How would you rate today?

1   2   3   4   5   6   7   8   9   10

If you want something you've never had then you have to do something you've never done before.

-Thomas Jefferson

Reflection

What it is that you want and what will you need to do differently to have it?

_____
_____
_____
_____
_____
_____
_____
_____
_____
_____
_____
_____
_____
_____
_____
_____

Intention

What is your intention for today? Just for today...

_____
_____

Meditation

How long did you meditate today? What type of meditation did you complete? Journal about today's meditation experience.

_____
_____
_____

Gratitude

Which three things are you grateful for today?

_____

_____

_____

Reading

Write one thought from today's reading that was meaningful to you.

_____

_____

_____

Exercise

Record how you chose to exercise today.

_____

_____

_____

Affirmations

Write three affirmations for today.

_____

_____

_____

Time for Self-Care

Reflect on what you did today to nourish your soul.

_____

_____

_____

How would you rate today?   1   2   3   4   5   6   7   8   9   10

One of the greatest feelings is accomplishing something that you once thought was impossible.

-Anonymous

Reflection

What was your biggest accomplishment and how did this accomplishment make you feel?

_____
_____
_____
_____
_____
_____
_____
_____
_____
_____
_____
_____
_____
_____
_____
_____

Intention

What is your intention for today? Just for today...

_____
_____

Meditation

How long did you meditate today? What type of meditation did you complete? Journal about today's meditation experience.

_____
_____
_____

Gratitude

Which three things are you grateful for today?

_____

_____

Reading

Write one thought from today's reading that was meaningful to you.

_____

_____

Exercise

Record how you chose to exercise today.

_____

_____

Affirmations

Write three affirmations for today.

_____

_____

Time for Self-Care

Reflect on what you did today to nourish your soul.

_____

_____

How would you rate today?

1   2   3   4   5   6   7   8   9   10

The two most important days in your life are the day that you were born and the day you find out why.

-Mark Twain

Reflection

What is your purpose in life? How will you share your purpose with others?

_____
_____
_____
_____
_____
_____
_____
_____
_____
_____
_____
_____
_____
_____

Intention

What is your intention for today? Just for today...

_____
_____

Meditation

How long did you meditate today? What type of meditation did you complete? Journal about today's meditation experience.

_____
_____
_____

Gratitude

Which three things are you grateful for today?

_____

_____

Reading

Write one thought from today's reading that was meaningful to you.

_____

_____

Exercise

Record how you chose to exercise today.

_____

_____

Affirmations

Write three affirmations for today.

_____

_____

Time for Self-Care

Reflect on what you did today to nourish your soul.

_____

_____

How would you rate today?

1   2   3   4   5   6   7   8   9   10

A ship is safe in harbor, but that's not what ships are for.
-William G.T. Shedd

Reflection

Describe a risk that you once took and explain what happened as a result.

_____
_____
_____
_____
_____
_____
_____
_____
_____
_____
_____
_____
_____
_____
_____
_____

Intention

What is your intention for today? Just for today...

_____
_____
_____

Meditation

How long did you meditate today? What type of meditation did you complete? Journal about today's meditation experience.

_____
_____
_____

Gratitude
Which three things are you grateful for today?

_____

_____

Reading
Write one thought from today's reading that was meaningful to you.

_____

_____

Exercise
Record how you chose to exercise today.

_____

_____

Affirmations
Write three affirmations for today.

_____

_____

Time for Self-Care
Reflect on what you did today to nourish your soul.

_____

_____

_____

How would you rate today?   1   2   3   4   5   6   7   8   9   10

Friends are angels that lift us to our feet when our wings have trouble remembering how to fly.

-Anonymous

Reflection

Describe a time when a friend helped you through a difficult time.

_____

_____

_____

_____

_____

_____

_____

_____

_____

_____

_____

_____

_____

_____

Intention

What is your intention for today? Just for today...

_____

_____

Meditation

How long did you meditate today? What type of meditation did you complete? Journal about today's meditation experience.

_____

_____

_____

Gratitude

Which three things are you grateful for today?

_____

_____

_____

Reading

Write one thought from today's reading that was meaningful to you.

_____

_____

_____

Exercise

Record how you chose to exercise today.

_____

_____

_____

Affirmations

Write three affirmations for today.

_____

_____

_____

Time for Self-Care

Reflect on what you did today to nourish your soul.

_____

_____

_____

How would you rate today?

1   2   3   4   5   6   7   8   9   10

Life begins at the end of your comfort zone.
-Anonymous

Reflection

Describe a time when you did something outside of your comfort zone. How did you feel afterwards?

_____

_____

_____

_____

_____

_____

_____

_____

_____

_____

_____

_____

_____

_____

_____

_____

_____

Intention

What is your intention for today? Just for today...

_____

_____

_____

Meditation

How long did you meditate today? What type of meditation did you complete? Journal about today's meditation experience.

_____

_____

_____

Gratitude

Which three things are you grateful for today?

_____

_____

_____

Reading

Write one thought from today's reading that was meaningful to you.

_____

_____

_____

Exercise

Record how you chose to exercise today.

_____

_____

_____

Affirmations

Write three affirmations for today.

_____

_____

_____

Time for Self-Care

Reflect on what you did today to nourish your soul.

_____

_____

_____

How would you rate today?

1   2   3   4   5   6   7   8   9   10

When you need something to believe in, start with yourself.

-Anonymous

Reflection

What are your best strengths? What do you do to encourage yourself?

_____

_____

_____

_____

_____

_____

_____

_____

_____

_____

_____

_____

_____

_____

_____

_____

Intention

What is your intention for today? Just for today...

_____

_____

_____

Meditation

How long did you meditate today? What type of meditation did you complete? Journal about today's meditation experience.

_____

_____

_____

Gratitude

Which three things are you grateful for today?

_____

_____

_____

Reading

Write one thought from today's reading that was meaningful to you.

_____

_____

_____

Exercise

Record how you chose to exercise today.

_____

_____

_____

Affirmations

Write three affirmations for today.

_____

_____

_____

Time for Self-Care

Reflect on what you did today to nourish your soul.

_____

_____

_____

How would you rate today?   1   2   3   4   5   6   7   8   9   10

Strive for progress, not perfection.
-Anonymous

Reflection

Think about a journey in your life. Write about where you started, the progress you've made, and where you finished.

_____

_____

_____

_____

_____

_____

_____

_____

_____

_____

_____

_____

_____

_____

_____

Intention

What is your intention for today? Just for today...

_____

_____

Meditation

How long did you meditate today? What type of meditation did you complete? Journal about today's meditation experience.

_____

_____

_____

Gratitude

Which three things are you grateful for today?

_____

_____

_____

Reading

Write one thought from today's reading that was meaningful to you.

_____

_____

_____

Exercise

Record how you chose to exercise today.

_____

_____

_____

Affirmations

Write three affirmations for today.

_____

_____

_____

Time for Self-Care

Reflect on what you did today to nourish your soul.

_____

_____

_____

How would you rate today?   1   2   3   4   5   6   7   8   9   10

My goal is to build a life I don't need a vacation from.
-Rob Hill

Reflection

Describe your ideal life.

_____

_____

_____

_____

_____

_____

_____

_____

_____

_____

_____

_____

_____

_____

Intention

What is your intention for today? Just for today...

_____

_____

Meditation

How long did you meditate today? What type of meditation did you complete? Journal about today's meditation experience.

_____

_____

_____

Gratitude

Which three things are you grateful for today?

_____

_____

_____

Reading

Write one thought from today's reading that was meaningful to you.

_____

_____

_____

Exercise

Record how you chose to exercise today.

_____

_____

_____

Affirmations

Write three affirmations for today.

_____

_____

_____

Time for Self-Care

Reflect on what you did today to nourish your soul.

_____

_____

_____

How would you rate today?   1   2   3   4   5   6   7   8   9   10

Art washes away from the soul the dust of everyday life.
-Pablo Picasso

Reflection

Everyone has a creative self. What are your creative talents?

_____
_____
_____
_____
_____
_____
_____
_____
_____
_____
_____
_____
_____
_____
_____

Intention

What is your intention for today? Just for today...

_____
_____

Meditation

How long did you meditate today? What type of meditation did you complete? Journal about today's meditation experience.

_____
_____
_____

Gratitude

Which three things are you grateful for today?

_____

_____

_____

Reading

Write one thought from today's reading that was meaningful to you.

_____

_____

_____

Exercise

Record how you chose to exercise today.

_____

_____

_____

Affirmations

Write three affirmations for today.

_____

_____

_____

Time for Self-Care

Reflect on what you did today to nourish your soul.

_____

_____

_____

How would you rate today?   1   2   3   4   5   6   7   8   9   10

Growing old is mandatory, but growing up is optional.
-Walt Disney

Reflection

Explain what you do to keep yourself feeling forever young.

_____

_____

_____

_____

_____

_____

_____

_____

_____

_____

_____

_____

_____

_____

_____

_____

Intention

What is your intention for today? Just for today...

_____

_____

Meditation

How long did you meditate today? What type of meditation did you complete? Journal about today's meditation experience.

_____

_____

_____

Gratitude

Which three things are you grateful for today?

_____

_____

_____

Reading

Write one thought from today's reading that was meaningful to you.

_____

_____

_____

Exercise

Record how you chose to exercise today.

_____

_____

_____

Affirmations

Write three affirmations for today.

_____

_____

_____

Time for Self-Care

Reflect on what you did today to nourish your soul.

_____

_____

_____

How would you rate today?   1   2   3   4   5   6   7   8   9   10

Family, like branches on a tree, we grow in different directions yet our roots remain as one.
-Anonymous

Reflection

How does your family keep you rooted?

_____
_____
_____
_____
_____
_____
_____
_____
_____
_____
_____
_____
_____
_____

Intention

What is your intention for today? Just for today...

_____
_____
_____

Meditation

How long did you meditate today? What type of meditation did you complete? Journal about today's meditation experience.

_____
_____
_____

Gratitude

Which three things are you grateful for today?

_____

_____

Reading

Write one thought from today's reading that was meaningful to you.

_____

_____

Exercise

Record how you chose to exercise today.

_____

_____

Affirmations

Write three affirmations for today.

_____

_____

Time for Self-Care

Reflect on what you did today to nourish your soul.

_____

_____

_____

How would you rate today?   1   2   3   4   5   6   7   8   9   10

Count your blessings, not your troubles.
-Anonymous

Reflection

What are your greatest blessings?

_____

_____

_____

_____

_____

_____

_____

_____

_____

_____

_____

_____

_____

_____

_____

_____

Intention

What is your intention for today? Just for today...

_____

_____

Meditation

How long did you meditate today? What type of meditation did you complete? Journal about today's meditation experience.

_____

_____

_____

Gratitude

Which three things are you grateful for today?

_____

_____

_____

Reading

Write one thought from today's reading that was meaningful to you.

_____

_____

_____

Exercise

Record how you chose to exercise today.

_____

_____

_____

Affirmations

Write three affirmations for today.

_____

_____

_____

Time for Self-Care

Reflect on what you did today to nourish your soul.

_____

_____

_____

How would you rate today?

1   2   3   4   5   6   7   8   9   10

Take Time to Reflect

It's been four weeks since you've first began this journal. Are you noticing any changes within yourself since starting your journey? Write about the changes that you have seen within yourself.

Take a moment to look back at this month's vision board. How successful were you in reaching your goals? Is there anything you need to do differently to make your dream happen?

_____
_____
_____
_____
_____
_____
_____
_____
_____
_____
_____
_____
_____
_____
_____
_____
_____
_____
_____
_____
_____
_____

PART
four

Welcome to a new month that's sure to be filled with new opportunities and possibilities. What will your goal be for this month? Do you want to begin working on a new goal or would you prefer to continue working on your goal from last month?

Once you've decided on this month's goal, you'll complete one of the goal worksheets. Afterwards, you'll have the opportunity to create another vision board.

Keep working toward your *dreams.*

My GOAL-SETTING Worksheet

Today's Date _____ **Goal Completion Date** _____

My goal is (be as specific as you can): _____
_____
_____

These are the steps I will need to take in order to achieve my goal:

1. _____
2. _____
3. _____
4. _____

When I am discouraged, I will remind myself why it's important to achieve this goal.

I want to achieve this goal because_____
_____
_____

I will track my progress here _____
_____
_____

When I achieve my goal, I will _____
_____
_____

S.M.A.R.T. GOALS *Worksheet*

Specific	What exactly do you want to accomplish?
Measurable	How will you track your progress?
Attainable	Do you have the skills and resources to attain this goal? What steps do you need to take to achieve your goal?
Relevant	Why is this goal important to you?
Timely	When do you want to complete this goal?

Create Your **Vision Board**

Can you believe it's already been one month since you've created your first vision board? How successful were you in reaching your goal?

It's now time to create this month's vision board. Do you want to continue working on the goal you set last month or would you prefer to work toward a new goal?

Once you decide on your goal, go ahead and create your vision board for this month.

Have fun, and remember to always keep working toward your dream.

You can use the box on the next page to practice your design. On the following two pages, you'll create your vision board for this month.

BOARD

Don't compare yourself to others. Compare yourself to the person you were yesterday.

-Anonymous

Reflection

What can you do to create a better version of yourself?

_____

_____

_____

_____

_____

_____

_____

_____

_____

_____

_____

_____

_____

_____

_____

Intention

What is your intention for today? Just for today...

_____

_____

_____

Meditation

How long did you meditate today? What type of meditation did you complete? Journal about today's meditation experience.

_____

_____

_____

Gratitude

Which three things are you grateful for today?

_____

_____

_____

Reading

Write one thought from today's reading that was meaningful to you.

_____

_____

_____

Exercise

Record how you chose to exercise today.

_____

_____

_____

Affirmations

Write three affirmations for today.

_____

_____

_____

Time for Self-Care

Reflect on what you did today to nourish your soul.

_____

_____

_____

How would you rate today?

1   2   3   4   5   6   7   8   9   10

Never be a prisoner of your past. It was just a lesson, not a life sentence.

-Anonymous

Reflection

What do you need to let go of in order to move forward?

_____

_____

_____

_____

_____

_____

_____

_____

_____

_____

_____

_____

_____

_____

_____

Intention

What is your intention for today? Just for today...

_____

_____

Meditation

How long did you meditate today? What type of meditation did you complete? Journal about today's meditation experience.

_____

_____

_____

Gratitude

Which three things are you grateful for today?

_____

_____

_____

Reading

Write one thought from today's reading that was meaningful to you.

_____

_____

_____

Exercise

Record how you chose to exercise today.

_____

_____

_____

Affirmations

Write three affirmations for today.

_____

_____

_____

Time for Self-Care

Reflect on what you did today to nourish your soul.

_____

_____

_____

How would you rate today?   1   2   3   4   5   6   7   8   9   10

Appreciate what you have before it turns into what you had.
-Anonymous

Reflection

Write about something you wished you had appreciated more while you still had it.

_____

_____

_____

_____

_____

_____

_____

_____

_____

_____

_____

_____

_____

_____

_____

Intention

What is your intention for today? Just for today...

_____

_____

_____

Meditation

How long did you meditate today? What type of meditation did you complete? Journal about today's meditation experience.

_____

_____

_____

Gratitude

Which three things are you grateful for today?

_____

_____

Reading

Write one thought from today's reading that was meaningful to you.

_____

_____

Exercise

Record how you chose to exercise today.

_____

_____

Affirmations

Write three affirmations for today.

_____

_____

Time for Self-Care

Reflect on what you did today to nourish your soul.

_____

_____

How would you rate today?   1   2   3   4   5   6   7   8   9   10

Whether you think you can or you think you can't, you're right.
-Henry Ford

Reflection

Are you optimistic or pessimistic by nature? Give an example.

_____

_____

_____

_____

_____

_____

_____

_____

_____

_____

_____

_____

_____

_____

_____

_____

Intention

What is your intention for today? Just for today...

_____

_____

_____

Meditation

How long did you meditate today? What type of meditation did you complete? Journal about today's meditation experience.

_____

_____

_____

Gratitude

Which three things are you grateful for today?

_____

_____

_____

Reading

Write one thought from today's reading that was meaningful to you.

_____

_____

_____

Exercise

Record how you chose to exercise today.

_____

_____

_____

Affirmations

Write three affirmations for today.

_____

_____

_____

Time for Self-Care

Reflect on what you did today to nourish your soul.

_____

_____

_____

How would you rate today?　　1　　2　　3　　4　　5　　6　　7　　8　　9　　10

Life is what happens when you're busy making other plans.
-John Lennon

Reflection

Describe a time in your life when things didn't go as planned. How did you handle the situation?

_____
_____
_____
_____
_____
_____
_____
_____
_____
_____
_____
_____
_____
_____
_____
_____
_____

Intention

What is your intention for today? Just for today...

_____
_____
_____

Meditation

How long did you meditate today? What type of meditation did you complete? Journal about today's meditation experience.

_____
_____
_____

Gratitude

Which three things are you grateful for today?

_____

_____

Reading

Write one thought from today's reading that was meaningful to you.

_____

_____

Exercise

Record how you chose to exercise today.

_____

_____

Affirmations

Write three affirmations for today.

_____

_____

Time for Self-Care

Reflect on what you did today to nourish your soul.

_____

_____

_____

How would you rate today?

1   2   3   4   5   6   7   8   9   10

Be yourself; everyone else is already taken.
-Oscar Wilde

Reflection

What are your most redeeming qualities?

_____

_____

_____

_____

_____

_____

_____

_____

_____

_____

_____

_____

_____

Intention

What is your intention for today? Just for today...

_____

_____

Meditation

How long did you meditate today? What type of meditation did you
complete? Journal about today's meditation experience.

_____

_____

_____

Gratitude

Which three things are you grateful for today?

_____

_____

_____

Reading

Write one thought from today's reading that was meaningful to you.

_____

_____

_____

Exercise

Record how you chose to exercise today.

_____

_____

_____

Affirmations

Write three affirmations for today.

_____

_____

_____

Time for Self-Care

Reflect on what you did today to nourish your soul.

_____

_____

_____

How would you rate today?

1   2   3   4   5   6   7   8   9   10

Time flies when you're having fun.
-Anonymous

Reflection

What was the most fun you've ever had? Describe what you did and who you were with.

_____

_____

_____

_____

_____

_____

_____

_____

_____

_____

_____

_____

_____

_____

_____

_____

Intention

What is your intention for today? Just for today...

_____

_____

_____

Meditation

How long did you meditate today? What type of meditation did you complete? Journal about today's meditation experience.

_____

_____

_____

Gratitude

Which three things are you grateful for today?

_____

_____

Reading

Write one thought from today's reading that was meaningful to you.

_____

_____

Exercise

Record how you chose to exercise today.

_____

_____

Affirmations

Write three affirmations for today.

_____

_____

Time for Self-Care

Reflect on what you did today to nourish your soul.

_____

_____

How would you rate today?

1   2   3   4   5   6   7   8   9   10

Worrying does not take away tomorrow's troubles. It takes away today's peace.

-Anonymous

Reflection

Describe the worries that are taking away from your peace today.

_____

_____

_____

_____

_____

_____

_____

_____

_____

_____

_____

_____

_____

_____

_____

Intention

What is your intention for today? Just for today...

_____

_____

Meditation

How long did you meditate today? What type of meditation did you complete? Journal about today's meditation experience.

_____

_____

_____

Gratitude

Which three things are you grateful for today?

_____

_____

_____

Reading

Write one thought from today's reading that was meaningful to you.

_____

_____

_____

Exercise

Record how you chose to exercise today.

_____

_____

_____

Affirmations

Write three affirmations for today.

_____

_____

_____

Time for Self-Care

Reflect on what you did today to nourish your soul.

_____

_____

_____

How would you rate today?

1   2   3   4   5   6   7   8   9   10

Striving for success without hard work is like trying to harvest where you haven't planted.

-David Bly

Reflection

How do you define success? What do you need to do in order to achieve it?

_____

_____

_____

_____

_____

_____

_____

_____

_____

_____

_____

_____

_____

_____

_____

_____

Intention

What is your intention for today? Just for today...

_____

_____

_____

Meditation

How long did you meditate today? What type of meditation did you complete? Journal about today's meditation experience.

_____

_____

_____

Gratitude

Which three things are you grateful for today?

_____

_____

Reading

Write one thought from today's reading that was meaningful to you.

_____

_____

Exercise

Record how you chose to exercise today.

_____

_____

Affirmations

Write three affirmations for today.

_____

_____

Time for Self-Care

Reflect on what you did today to nourish your soul.

_____

_____

How would you rate today?   1   2   3   4   5   6   7   8   9   10

If it's important to you, you'll find a way. If not, you'll find an excuse.
-Ryan Blair

Reflection

Are you more apt to find a way or an excuse? Explain why and give an example.

_____
_____
_____
_____
_____
_____
_____
_____
_____
_____
_____
_____
_____
_____
_____

Intention

What is your intention for today? Just for today...

_____
_____

Meditation

How long did you meditate today? What type of meditation did you complete? Journal about today's meditation experience.

_____
_____
_____

Gratitude

Which three things are you grateful for today?

_____

_____

Reading

Write one thought from today's reading that was meaningful to you.

_____

_____

Exercise

Record how you chose to exercise today.

_____

_____

Affirmations

Write three affirmations for today.

_____

_____

Time for Self-Care

Reflect on what you did today to nourish your soul.

_____

_____

How would you rate today?

1   2   3   4   5   6   7   8   9   10

Forgiveness does not change the past, but it does change the future.

-Anonymous

Reflection

Who do you need to forgive in order to move forward?

_____
_____
_____
_____
_____
_____
_____
_____
_____
_____
_____
_____
_____
_____
_____

Intention

What is your intention for today? Just for today...

_____
_____

Meditation

How long did you meditate today? What type of meditation did you complete? Journal about today's meditation experience.

_____
_____
_____

Gratitude

Which three things are you grateful for today?

_____

_____

Reading

Write one thought from today's reading that was meaningful to you.

_____

_____

Exercise

Record how you chose to exercise today.

_____

_____

Affirmations

Write three affirmations for today.

_____

_____

Time for Self-Care

Reflect on what you did today to nourish your soul.

_____

_____

How would you rate today?

1   2   3   4   5   6   7   8   9   10

You can't expect to see change if you never do anything differently.

-Meg Biram

Reflection

What change do you need to make to improve your life?

_____

_____

_____

_____

_____

_____

_____

_____

_____

_____

_____

_____

_____

_____

Intention

What is your intention for today? Just for today...

_____

_____

Meditation

How long did you meditate today? What type of meditation did you complete? Journal about today's meditation experience.

_____

_____

_____

Gratitude

Which three things are you grateful for today?

_____

_____

Reading

Write one thought from today's reading that was meaningful to you.

_____

_____

Exercise

Record how you chose to exercise today.

_____

_____

Affirmations

Write three affirmations for today.

_____

_____

Time for Self-Care

Reflect on what you did today to nourish your soul.

_____

_____

How would you rate today?   1   2   3   4   5   6   7   8   9   10

Strive not to be a success, but rather to be of value.

-Albert Einstein

Reflection

What virtues do you deem most valuable for success? Do you possess these values?

_____

_____

_____

_____

_____

_____

_____

_____

_____

_____

_____

_____

_____

_____

_____

Intention

What is your intention for today? Just for today...

_____

_____

Meditation

How long did you meditate today? What type of meditation did you complete? Journal about today's meditation experience.

_____

_____

_____

Gratitude

Which three things are you grateful for today?

_____

_____

_____

Reading

Write one thought from today's reading that was meaningful to you.

_____

_____

_____

Exercise

Record how you chose to exercise today.

_____

_____

_____

Affirmations

Write three affirmations for today.

_____

_____

_____

Time for Self-Care

Reflect on what you did today to nourish your soul.

_____

_____

_____

How would you rate today?   1   2   3   4   5   6   7   8   9   10

Stop saying I wish and start saying I will.
-Anonymous

Reflection

What do you need to do to make your wish happen?

_____

_____

_____

_____

_____

_____

_____

_____

_____

_____

_____

_____

_____

_____

Intention

What is your intention for today? Just for today...

_____

_____

Meditation

How long did you meditate today? What type of meditation did you complete? Journal about today's meditation experience.

_____

_____

_____

Gratitude

Which three things are you grateful for today?

_____

_____

_____

Reading

Write one thought from today's reading that was meaningful to you.

_____

_____

_____

Exercise

Record how you chose to exercise today.

_____

_____

_____

Affirmations

Write three affirmations for today.

_____

_____

_____

Time for Self-Care

Reflect on what you did today to nourish your soul.

_____

_____

_____

How would you rate today?

1   2   3   4   5   6   7   8   9   10

It's not how we make mistakes, but how we correct them that defines us.

-Anonymous

Reflection

What was your biggest mistake? What did you do to correct your mistake? What did you learn from your mistake?

_____

_____

_____

_____

_____

_____

_____

_____

_____

_____

_____

_____

_____

_____

Intention

What is your intention for today? Just for today...

_____

_____

_____

Meditation

How long did you meditate today? What type of meditation did you complete? Journal about today's meditation experience.

_____

_____

_____

Gratitude

Which three things are you grateful for today?

_____

_____

_____

Reading

Write one thought from today's reading that was meaningful to you.

_____

_____

_____

Exercise

Record how you chose to exercise today.

_____

_____

_____

Affirmations

Write three affirmations for today.

_____

_____

_____

Time for Self-Care

Reflect on what you did today to nourish your soul.

_____

_____

_____

How would you rate today?   1   2   3   4   5   6   7   8   9   10

It's not what happens to you, but how you react to it that matters.
-Epictetus

Reflection

How do you usually react to a stressful situation? Do you tend to panic or remain calm? How have your reactions in life shaped you into the person you are today?

_____

_____

_____

_____

_____

_____

_____

_____

_____

_____

_____

_____

_____

_____

_____

_____

Intention

What is your intention for today? Just for today...

_____

_____

Meditation

How long did you meditate today? What type of meditation did you complete? Journal about today's meditation experience.

_____

_____

_____

Gratitude

Which three things are you grateful for today?

_____

_____

_____

Reading

Write one thought from today's reading that was meaningful to you.

_____

_____

_____

Exercise

Record how you chose to exercise today.

_____

_____

_____

Affirmations

Write three affirmations for today.

_____

_____

_____

Time for Self-Care

Reflect on what you did today to nourish your soul.

_____

_____

_____

How would you rate today? 1   2   3   4   5   6   7   8   9   10

Being brave means doing what you're afraid to do.
-Anonymous

Reflection

What was the bravest thing you ever had to do?

_____

_____

_____

_____

_____

_____

_____

_____

_____

_____

_____

_____

_____

_____

_____

Intention

What is your intention for today? Just for today...

_____

_____

Meditation

How long did you meditate today? What type of meditation did you complete? Journal about today's meditation experience.

_____

_____

Gratitude

Which three things are you grateful for today?

_____

_____

Reading

Write one thought from today's reading that was meaningful to you.

_____

_____

Exercise

Record how you chose to exercise today.

_____

_____

Affirmations

Write three affirmations for today.

_____

_____

Time for Self-Care

Reflect on what you did today to nourish your soul.

_____

_____

_____

How would you rate today?

1   2   3   4   5   6   7   8   9   10

A walk in nature walks the soul back home.
-Anonymous

Reflection

How do you most enjoy spending time with nature? Describe how you feel after spending time with nature.

_____

_____

_____

_____

_____

_____

_____

_____

_____

_____

_____

_____

_____

Intention

What is your intention for today? Just for today...

_____

_____

Meditation

How long did you meditate today? What type of meditation did you complete? Journal about today's meditation experience.

_____

_____

_____

Gratitude

Which three things are you grateful for today?

_____

_____

Reading

Write one thought from today's reading that was meaningful to you.

_____

_____

Exercise

Record how you chose to exercise today.

_____

_____

Affirmations

Write three affirmations for today.

_____

_____

Time for Self-Care

Reflect on what you did today to nourish your soul.

_____

_____

How would you rate today?   1   2   3   4   5   6   7   8   9   10

Be the role model you needed when you were younger.
-Anonymous

Reflection

Who was the most influential role model in your life? What important lessons did you learn from this person?

_____
_____
_____
_____
_____
_____
_____
_____
_____
_____
_____
_____
_____
_____
_____
_____

Intention

What is your intention for today? Just for today...

_____
_____

Meditation

How long did you meditate today? What type of meditation did you complete? Journal about today's meditation experience.

_____
_____
_____

Gratitude

Which three things are you grateful for today?

_____

_____

_____

Reading

Write one thought from today's reading that was meaningful to you.

_____

_____

_____

Exercise

Record how you chose to exercise today.

_____

_____

_____

Affirmations

Write three affirmations for today.

_____

_____

_____

Time for Self-Care

Reflect on what you did today to nourish your soul.

_____

_____

_____

How would you rate today?   1   2   3   4   5   6   7   8   9   10

Hope is seeing light in spite of the darkness.
-Desmond Tutu

Reflection

Describe a time when hope helped you to get through a dark time.

_____

_____

_____

_____

_____

_____

_____

_____

_____

_____

_____

_____

_____

_____

Intention

What is your intention for today? Just for today...

_____

_____

Meditation

How long did you meditate today? What type of meditation did you complete? Journal about today's meditation experience.

_____

_____

_____

Gratitude

Which three things are you grateful for today?

_____

_____

_____

Reading

Write one thought from today's reading that was meaningful to you.

_____

_____

_____

Exercise

Record how you chose to exercise today.

_____

_____

_____

Affirmations

Write three affirmations for today.

_____

_____

_____

Time for Self-Care

Reflect on what you did today to nourish your soul.

_____

_____

_____

How would you rate today?

1   2   3   4   5   6   7   8   9   10

The way we talk to our children becomes their inner voice.
-Peggy O'Mara

Reflection

How did your parents speak to you as a child? Were their words hurtful or encouraging? How have their words shaped you into the person you are today? If you are a parent now, do you speak to your children in the same way or differently? Explain.

_____

_____

_____

_____

_____

_____

_____

_____

_____

_____

_____

_____

Intention

What is your intention for today? Just for today...

_____

_____

Meditation

How long did you meditate today? What type of meditation did you complete? Journal about today's meditation experience.

_____

_____

_____

Gratitude

Which three things are you grateful for today?

_____

_____

_____

Reading

Write one thought from today's reading that was meaningful to you.

_____

_____

_____

Exercise

Record how you chose to exercise today.

_____

_____

_____

Affirmations

Write three affirmations for today.

_____

_____

_____

Time for Self-Care

Reflect on what you did today to nourish your soul.

_____

_____

_____

How would you rate today?   1   2   3   4   5   6   7   8   9   10

It is not the gift, but the thought that counts.
-Henry Van Dyke

Reflection

What was the most meaningful gift you've ever received? Explain why this gift was important to you and who the gift was from.

_____

_____

_____

_____

_____

_____

_____

_____

_____

_____

_____

_____

_____

_____

Intention

What is your intention for today? Just for today...

_____

_____

_____

Meditation

How long did you meditate today? What type of meditation did you complete? Journal about today's meditation experience.

_____

_____

_____

Gratitude

Which three things are you grateful for today?

_____

_____

_____

Reading

Write one thought from today's reading that was meaningful to you.

_____

_____

_____

Exercise

Record how you chose to exercise today.

_____

_____

_____

Affirmations

Write three affirmations for today.

_____

_____

_____

Time for Self-Care

Reflect on what you did today to nourish your soul.

_____

_____

_____

How would you rate today?

1   2   3   4   5   6   7   8   9   10

Sometimes memories sneak out of my eyes and roll down my cheeks.
    -Anonymous

Reflection

Which memories from your childhood caused you to cry? Were your tears a result of happiness, sadness, or anger? Explain.

_____

_____

_____

_____

_____

_____

_____

_____

_____

_____

_____

_____

_____

_____

Intention

What is your intention for today? Just for today...

_____

_____

_____

Meditation

How long did you meditate today? What type of meditation did you complete? Journal about today's meditation experience.

_____

_____

_____

Gratitude

Which three things are you grateful for today?

_____

_____

_____

Reading

Write one thought from today's reading that was meaningful to you.

_____

_____

_____

Exercise

Record how you chose to exercise today.

_____

_____

_____

Affirmations

Write three affirmations for today.

_____

_____

_____

Time for Self-Care

Reflect on what you did today to nourish your soul.

_____

_____

_____

How would you rate today?   1   2   3   4   5   6   7   8   9   10

There are magical moments in every day. We just have to take the time to see them.

-Anonymous

Reflection

Describe a magical moment in your life.

_____

_____

_____

_____

_____

_____

_____

_____

_____

_____

_____

_____

_____

_____

_____

_____

Intention

What is your intention for today? Just for today...

_____

_____

Meditation

How long did you meditate today? What type of meditation did you complete? Journal about today's meditation experience.

_____

_____

_____

Gratitude

Which three things are you grateful for today?

_____

_____

_____

Reading

Write one thought from today's reading that was meaningful to you.

_____

_____

_____

Exercise

Record how you chose to exercise today.

_____

_____

_____

Affirmations

Write three affirmations for today.

_____

_____

_____

Time for Self-Care

Reflect on what you did today to nourish your soul.

_____

_____

_____

How would you rate today?

1   2   3   4   5   6   7   8   9   10

Heroes are made by the paths they choose, not the powers they are graced with.

-Anonymous

Reflection

What does a hero mean to you? Is there a hero in your life? Explain.

_____

_____

_____

_____

_____

_____

_____

_____

_____

_____

_____

_____

_____

_____

_____

_____

Intention

What is your intention for today? Just for today...

_____

_____

_____

Meditation

How long did you meditate today? What type of meditation did you complete? Journal about today's meditation experience.

_____

_____

_____

Gratitude

Which three things are you grateful for today?

_____

_____

Reading

Write one thought from today's reading that was meaningful to you.

_____

_____

Exercise

Record how you chose to exercise today.

_____

_____

Affirmations

Write three affirmations for today.

_____

_____

Time for Self-Care

Reflect on what you did today to nourish your soul.

_____

_____

_____

How would you rate today?   1   2   3   4   5   6   7   8   9   10

Now is the best time to start becoming the person you want to be remembered as.

-Dieter F. Uchtdorf

Reflection

How you do most want to be remembered?

_____

_____

_____

_____

_____

_____

_____

_____

_____

_____

_____

_____

_____

_____

_____

Intention

What is your intention for today? Just for today...

_____

_____

Meditation

How long did you meditate today? What type of meditation did you complete? Journal about today's meditation experience.

_____

_____

_____

Gratitude

Which three things are you grateful for today?

_____

_____

_____

Reading

Write one thought from today's reading that was meaningful to you.

_____

_____

_____

Exercise

Record how you chose to exercise today.

_____

_____

_____

Affirmations

Write three affirmations for today.

_____

_____

_____

Time for Self-Care

Reflect on what you did today to nourish your soul.

_____

_____

_____

How would you rate today?   1   2   3   4   5   6   7   8   9   10

Scars tell the story of where you've been. They don't dictate where you are going.

-Anonymous

Reflection

Are your scars visible or invisible? What stories do they tell?

_____

_____

_____

_____

_____

_____

_____

_____

_____

_____

_____

_____

_____

_____

_____

Intention

What is your intention for today? Just for today...

_____

_____

_____

Meditation

How long did you meditate today? What type of meditation did you complete? Journal about today's meditation experience.

_____

_____

_____

Gratitude

Which three things are you grateful for today?

_____

_____

Reading

Write one thought from today's reading that was meaningful to you.

_____

_____

Exercise

Record how you chose to exercise today.

_____

_____

Affirmations

Write three affirmations for today.

_____

_____

Time for Self-Care

Reflect on what you did today to nourish your soul.

_____

_____

_____

How would you rate today?   1   2   3   4   5   6   7   8   9   10

Pain of mind is worse than pain of body

-Publilus Syrus

Reflection

What was the worse pain you've ever had to endure? Was your pain physical or emotional?

_____

_____

_____

_____

_____

_____

_____

_____

_____

_____

_____

_____

_____

_____

Intention

What is your intention for today? Just for today...

_____

_____

_____

Meditation

How long did you meditate today? What type of meditation did you complete? Journal about today's meditation experience.

_____

_____

_____

Gratitude

Which three things are you grateful for today?

_____

_____

_____

Reading

Write one thought from today's reading that was meaningful to you.

_____

_____

_____

Exercise

Record how you chose to exercise today.

_____

_____

_____

Affirmations

Write three affirmations for today.

_____

_____

_____

Time for Self-Care

Reflect on what you did today to nourish your soul.

_____

_____

_____

How would you rate today?   1   2   3   4   5   6   7   8   9   10

It's hard to accept the truth when the lies were exactly what you wanted to hear.

-Anonymous

Reflection

What was the most difficult truth you ever had to accept?

_____

_____

_____

_____

_____

_____

_____

_____

_____

_____

_____

_____

_____

_____

_____

_____

Intention

What is your intention for today? Just for today...

_____

_____

_____

Meditation

How long did you meditate today? What type of meditation did you complete? Journal about today's meditation experience.

_____

_____

_____

Gratitude

Which three things are you grateful for today?

_____

_____

_____

Reading

Write one thought from today's reading that was meaningful to you.

_____

_____

_____

Exercise

Record how you chose to exercise today.

_____

_____

_____

Affirmations

Write three affirmations for today.

_____

_____

_____

Time for Self-Care

Reflect on what you did today to nourish your soul.

_____

_____

_____

How would you rate today?   1   2   3   4   5   6   7   8   9   10

Childhood memories can't be taken away from you.
-Anonymous

Reflection

What are the best and worst memories from your childhood?

_____

_____

_____

_____

_____

_____

_____

_____

_____

_____

_____

_____

_____

_____

_____

Intention

What is your intention for today? Just for today...

_____

_____

Meditation

How long did you meditate today? What type of meditation did you complete? Journal about today's meditation experience.

_____

_____

_____

Gratitude
Which three things are you grateful for today?

_____

_____

_____

Reading
Write one thought from today's reading that was meaningful to you.

_____

_____

_____

Exercise
Record how you chose to exercise today.

_____

_____

_____

Affirmations
Write three affirmations for today.

_____

_____

_____

Time for Self-Care
Reflect on what you did today to nourish your soul.

_____

_____

_____

How would you rate today?
1   2   3   4   5   6   7   8   9   10

Take Time to Reflect

Congratulations! You are now more than half way through your journey of self-discovery.

What truths have you learned about yourself since you first began your journey? What strengths and weaknesses have you discovered? Where have you seen self-growth? Where do you still need to grow?

Were you successful in achieving this month's goal? If so, how did you celebrate your success? If not, what changes do you need to make in order to be successful?

_____

_____

_____

_____

_____

_____

_____

_____

_____

_____

_____

_____

_____

_____

_____

_____

_____

_____

PART
five

WOW! It's been two months since you began your journey of self-discovery. Look at all you've learned about yourself and how you have grown.

How are you progressing with your goals? Are you happy with the progress you're making or do you need to work harder at your goals?

What goal will you set for yourself this month? Will it be a new goal or will you continue to work on your goal from last month?

Once you have decided on your goal for this month, complete one of the goal worksheets. Afterwards, you'll have the opportunity to create another vision board.

Remember to
have fun
and keep
working
toward your
dreams.

My GOAL-SETTING Worksheet

Today's Date _____ **Goal Completion Date** _____

My goal is (be as specific as you can): _____

_____

_____

These are the steps I will need to take in order to achieve my goal:

1. _____
2. _____
3. _____
4. _____

When I am discouraged, I will remind myself why it's important to achieve this goal.

I want to achieve this goal because _____

_____

_____

I will track my progress here _____

_____

_____

When I achieve my goal, I will _____

_____

_____

S.M.A.R.T. GOALS *Worksheet*

Specific	What exactly do you want to accomplish?
Measurable	How can you break your goal into manageable steps? How will you track your progress?
Attainable	Do you have the skills and resources to attain this goal? What steps do you need to take to achieve your goal?
Relevant	Why is this goal important to you?
Timely	When do you want to complete this goal?

Create Your **Vision Board**

Once again, it's time to create a vision board that will inspire you and keep you reaching toward your goal. Adding inspirational quotes and pictures to your vision board will help you to remain on track so you can achieve your dreams.

Be sure to post your vision board in a prominent place so that you can refer to it often. The more you visualize your goal, the easier it will be to obtain.

You can use the box on the next page to practice your design. On the following two pages, you'll create your vision board for this month.

VISION

BOARD

Everyone you know is fighting a battle you know nothing about. Be kind always.

-Anonymous

Reflection

Are there any battles that you're fighting? How have your battles changed you?

_____
_____
_____
_____
_____
_____
_____
_____
_____
_____
_____
_____
_____
_____
_____
_____

Intention

What is your intention for today? Just for today...

_____
_____
_____

Meditation

How long did you meditate today? What type of meditation did you complete? Journal about today's meditation experience.

_____
_____
_____

Gratitude
Which three things are you grateful for today?

_____

_____

_____

Reading
Write one thought from today's reading that was meaningful to you.

_____

_____

_____

Exercise
Record how you chose to exercise today.

_____

_____

_____

Affirmations
Write three affirmations for today.

_____

_____

_____

Time for Self-Care
Reflect on what you did today to nourish your soul.

_____

_____

_____

How would you rate today? 1   2   3   4   5   6   7   8   9   10

Stop being afraid of what could go wrong and start thinking about what could go right.

-Anonymous

Reflection

Write a list of all the things you have done right in your life.

_____

_____

_____

_____

_____

_____

_____

_____

_____

_____

_____

_____

_____

_____

_____

_____

Intention

What is your intention for today? Just for today...

_____

_____

_____

Meditation

How long did you meditate today? What type of meditation did you complete? Journal about today's meditation experience.

_____

_____

_____

Gratitude

Which three things are you grateful for today?

_____

_____

_____

Reading

Write one thought from today's reading that was meaningful to you.

_____

_____

_____

Exercise

Record how you chose to exercise today.

_____

_____

_____

Affirmations

Write three affirmations for today.

_____

_____

_____

Time for Self-Care

Reflect on what you did today to nourish your soul.

_____

_____

_____

How would you rate today?   1   2   3   4   5   6   7   8   9   10

Everything you've ever wanted is on the other side of fear.
-George Addair

Reflection

What are you most afraid of? How is your fear preventing you from getting what you truly want?

_____
_____
_____
_____
_____
_____
_____
_____
_____
_____
_____
_____
_____
_____
_____
_____

Intention

What is your intention for today? Just for today...

_____
_____
_____

Meditation

How long did you meditate today? What type of meditation did you complete? Journal about today's meditation experience.

_____
_____
_____

Gratitude

Which three things are you grateful for today?

_____

_____

_____

Reading

Write one thought from today's reading that was meaningful to you.

_____

_____

_____

Exercise

Record how you chose to exercise today.

_____

_____

_____

Affirmations

Write three affirmations for today.

_____

_____

_____

Time for Self-Care

Reflect on what you did today to nourish your soul.

_____

_____

_____

How would you rate today?   1   2   3   4   5   6   7   8   9   10

One reason why people resist change is because they focus on what they have to give up instead of what they have to gain.

-Rick Godwin

Reflection

What one change would you most want to see in yourself? What do you have to gain from this change?

_____

_____

_____

_____

_____

_____

_____

_____

_____

_____

_____

_____

_____

_____

Intention

What is your intention for today? Just for today...

_____

_____

Meditation

How long did you meditate today? What type of meditation did you complete? Journal about today's meditation experience.

_____

_____

_____

Gratitude

Which three things are you grateful for today?

_____

_____

_____

Reading

Write one thought from today's reading that was meaningful to you.

_____

_____

_____

Exercise

Record how you chose to exercise today.

_____

_____

_____

Affirmations

Write three affirmations for today.

_____

_____

_____

Time for Self-Care

Reflect on what you did today to nourish your soul.

_____

_____

_____

How would you rate today?   1   2   3   4   5   6   7   8   9   10

Follow your passion; it will lead you to your purpose.
-Oprah Winfrey

Reflection

What are you most passionate about? How can you share your passion with others?

_____
_____
_____
_____
_____
_____
_____
_____
_____
_____
_____
_____
_____
_____
_____

Intention

What is your intention for today? Just for today...

_____
_____
_____

Meditation

How long did you meditate today? What type of meditation did you complete? Journal about today's meditation experience.

_____
_____
_____

Gratitude

Which three things are you grateful for today?

_____

_____

_____

Reading

Write one thought from today's reading that was meaningful to you.

_____

_____

_____

Exercise

Record how you chose to exercise today.

_____

_____

_____

Affirmations

Write three affirmations for today.

_____

_____

_____

Time for Self-Care

Reflect on what you did today to nourish your soul.

_____

_____

_____

How would you rate today?   1   2   3   4   5   6   7   8   9   10

Stop, take a moment, look around you, and appreciate the beauty in your life.

-Gail Lynne Goodwin

Reflection

Where do you find beauty in your everyday life?

_____

_____

_____

_____

_____

_____

_____

_____

_____

_____

_____

_____

_____

_____

_____

_____

Intention

What is your intention for today? Just for today...

_____

_____

_____

Meditation

How long did you meditate today? What type of meditation did you complete? Journal about today's meditation experience.

_____

_____

_____

Gratitude

Which three things are you grateful for today?

_____

_____

_____

Reading

Write one thought from today's reading that was meaningful to you.

_____

_____

_____

Exercise

Record how you chose to exercise today.

_____

_____

_____

Affirmations

Write three affirmations for today.

_____

_____

_____

Time for Self-Care

Reflect on what you did today to nourish your soul.

_____

_____

_____

How would you rate today?

1   2   3   4   5   6   7   8   9   10

Life isn't about waiting for the storm to pass. It's about learning to dance in the rain.

-Anonymous

Reflection

Describe a time when you needed to make the best of a bad situation.

_____

_____

_____

_____

_____

_____

_____

_____

_____

_____

_____

_____

_____

_____

_____

_____

Intention

What is your intention for today? Just for today...

_____

_____

_____

Meditation

How long did you meditate today? What type of meditation did you complete? Journal about today's meditation experience.

_____

_____

_____

Gratitude

Which three things are you grateful for today?

_____

_____

_____

Reading

Write one thought from today's reading that was meaningful to you.

_____

_____

_____

Exercise

Record how you chose to exercise today.

_____

_____

_____

Affirmations

Write three affirmations for today.

_____

_____

_____

Time for Self-Care

Reflect on what you did today to nourish your soul.

_____

_____

_____

How would you rate today?   1   2   3   4   5   6   7   8   9   10

Stand up to what is right even if it means standing alone.
-Anonymous

Reflection

Was there ever a time in your life when you stood up for what you believed to be right? Explain.

_____

_____

_____

_____

_____

_____

_____

_____

_____

_____

_____

_____

_____

_____

_____

Intention

What is your intention for today? Just for today...

_____

_____

Meditation

How long did you meditate today? What type of meditation did you complete? Journal about today's meditation experience.

_____

_____

_____

Gratitude

Which three things are you grateful for today?

_____

_____

_____

Reading

Write one thought from today's reading that was meaningful to you.

_____

_____

_____

Exercise

Record how you chose to exercise today.

_____

_____

_____

Affirmations

Write three affirmations for today.

_____

_____

_____

Time for Self-Care

Reflect on what you did today to nourish your soul.

_____

_____

_____

How would you rate today?

1   2   3   4   5   6   7   8   9   10

Paradise isn't a place. It's a state of mind.
-Frank Sonnenberg

Reflection

Describe what you do to find peace of mind.

_____
_____
_____
_____
_____
_____
_____
_____
_____
_____
_____
_____
_____
_____
_____
_____

Intention

What is your intention for today? Just for today...

_____
_____
_____

Meditation

How long did you meditate today? What type of meditation did you
complete? Journal about today's meditation experience.

_____
_____
_____

Gratitude
Which three things are you grateful for today?

_____

_____

Reading
Write one thought from today's reading that was meaningful to you.

_____

_____

Exercise
Record how you chose to exercise today.

_____

_____

Affirmations
Write three affirmations for today.

_____

_____

Time for Self-Care
Reflect on what you did today to nourish your soul.

_____

_____

How would you rate today?
1   2   3   4   5   6   7   8   9   10

Each moment of the year has its own beauty.
-Ralph Waldo Emerson

Reflection

What is your favorite season of the year and why? Write a poem describing the beauty of your favorite season.

_____

_____

_____

_____

_____

_____

_____

_____

_____

_____

_____

_____

_____

_____

_____

Intention

What is your intention for today? Just for today...

_____

_____

Meditation

How long did you meditate today? What type of meditation did you complete? Journal about today's meditation experience.

_____

_____

_____

Gratitude

Which three things are you grateful for today?

_____

_____

_____

Reading

Write one thought from today's reading that was meaningful to you.

_____

_____

_____

Exercise

Record how you chose to exercise today.

_____

_____

_____

Affirmations

Write three affirmations for today.

_____

_____

_____

Time for Self-Care

Reflect on what you did today to nourish your soul.

_____

_____

_____

How would you rate today?   1   2   3   4   5   6   7   8   9   10

Difficult roads often lead to beautiful destinations.

-Anonymous

Reflection

Describe a difficult journey in your life that brought you to a better place.

_____
_____
_____
_____
_____
_____
_____
_____
_____
_____
_____
_____
_____
_____
_____

Intention

What is your intention for today? Just for today...

_____
_____

Meditation

How long did you meditate today? What type of meditation did you complete? Journal about today's meditation experience.

_____
_____
_____

Gratitude
Which three things are you grateful for today?

_____

_____

_____

Reading
Write one thought from today's reading that was meaningful to you.

_____

_____

_____

Exercise
Record how you chose to exercise today.

_____

_____

_____

Affirmations
Write three affirmations for today.

_____

_____

_____

Time for Self-Care
Reflect on what you did today to nourish your soul.

_____

_____

_____

How would you rate today?
1   2   3   4   5   6   7   8   9   10

Life takes you to unexpected places. Love brings you home.
-Anonymous

Reflection

What unexpected places has your life taken you to? What brought you home?

_____

_____

_____

_____

_____

_____

_____

_____

_____

_____

_____

_____

_____

_____

_____

_____

Intention

What is your intention for today? Just for today...

_____

_____

Meditation

How long did you meditate today? What type of meditation did you complete? Journal about today's meditation experience.

_____

_____

_____

Gratitude

Which three things are you grateful for today?

_____

_____

_____

Reading

Write one thought from today's reading that was meaningful to you.

_____

_____

_____

Exercise

Record how you chose to exercise today.

_____

_____

_____

Affirmations

Write three affirmations for today.

_____

_____

_____

Time for Self-Care

Reflect on what you did today to nourish your soul.

_____

_____

_____

How would you rate today?

1   2   3   4   5   6   7   8   9   10

Not friends, not enemies, just strangers with some memories.
-Anonymous

Reflection

Describe a relationship that was meaningful to you. What happened to change the relationship? How has this change affected you?

_____

_____

_____

_____

_____

_____

_____

_____

_____

_____

_____

_____

_____

Intention

What is your intention for today? Just for today...

_____

_____

_____

Meditation

How long did you meditate today? What type of meditation did you complete? Journal about today's meditation experience.

_____

_____

_____

Gratitude

Which three things are you grateful for today?

_____

_____

_____

Reading

Write one thought from today's reading that was meaningful to you.

_____

_____

_____

Exercise

Record how you chose to exercise today.

_____

_____

_____

Affirmations

Write three affirmations for today.

_____

_____

_____

Time for Self-Care

Reflect on what you did today to nourish your soul.

_____

_____

_____

How would you rate today?   1   2   3   4   5   6   7   8   9   10

The most treasured heirlooms are the sweet memories of our family that we pass down to our children.

-Anonymous

Reflection

What family traditions are most precious to you and why?

_____

_____

_____

_____

_____

_____

_____

_____

_____

_____

_____

_____

_____

_____

_____

_____

Intention

What is your intention for today? Just for today...

_____

_____

Meditation

How long did you meditate today? What type of meditation did you complete? Journal about today's meditation experience.

_____

_____

_____

Gratitude
Which three things are you grateful for today?

_____

_____

Reading
Write one thought from today's reading that was meaningful to you.

_____

_____

Exercise
Record how you chose to exercise today.

_____

_____

Affirmations
Write three affirmations for today.

_____

_____

Time for Self-Care
Reflect on what you did today to nourish your soul.

_____

_____

How would you rate today?   1   2   3   4   5   6   7   8   9   10

We all carry with us the people that came before us.
-Liam Callanan

Reflection

How have the struggles and triumphs of your ancestors shaped you into the person you are today? Who from your family has been the biggest influence in your life?

_____
_____
_____
_____
_____
_____
_____
_____
_____
_____
_____
_____
_____
_____

Intention

What is your intention for today? Just for today...

_____
_____

Meditation

How long did you meditate today? What type of meditation did you complete? Journal about today's meditation experience.

_____
_____
_____

Gratitude

Which three things are you grateful for today?

_____

_____

_____

Reading

Write one thought from today's reading that was meaningful to you.

_____

_____

_____

Exercise

Record how you chose to exercise today.

_____

_____

_____

Affirmations

Write three affirmations for today.

_____

_____

_____

Time for Self-Care

Reflect on what you did today to nourish your soul.

_____

_____

_____

How would you rate today?   1   2   3   4   5   6   7   8   9   10

Children learn more from what you are than what you teach.
-W.E.B. Du Bois

Reflection

What important lessons did you learn from your parents? If you are a parent now, what lessons do you want your children to learn from you?

_____

_____

_____

_____

_____

_____

_____

_____

_____

_____

_____

_____

_____

_____

_____

Intention

What is your intention for today? Just for today...

_____

_____

Meditation

How long did you meditate today? What type of meditation did you complete? Journal about today's meditation experience.

_____

_____

_____

Gratitude

Which three things are you grateful for today?

_____

_____

Reading

Write one thought from today's reading that was meaningful to you.

_____

_____

Exercise

Record how you chose to exercise today.

_____

_____

Affirmations

Write three affirmations for today.

_____

_____

Time for Self-Care

Reflect on what you did today to nourish your soul.

_____

_____

How would you rate today?   1   2   3   4   5   6   7   8   9   10

Nothing is impossible; the word itself says "I'm possible."
-Audrey Hepburn

Reflection

Describe something you did that you never thought possible.

_____
_____
_____
_____
_____
_____
_____
_____
_____
_____
_____
_____
_____
_____

Intention

What is your intention for today? Just for today...

_____
_____

Meditation

How long did you meditate today? What type of meditation did you complete? Journal about today's meditation experience.

_____
_____
_____

Gratitude

Which three things are you grateful for today?

_____

_____

_____

Reading

Write one thought from today's reading that was meaningful to you.

_____

_____

_____

Exercise

Record how you chose to exercise today.

_____

_____

_____

Affirmations

Write three affirmations for today.

_____

_____

_____

Time for Self-Care

Reflect on what you did today to nourish your soul.

_____

_____

_____

How would you rate today?

1   2   3   4   5   6   7   8   9   10

Yesterday is history. Tomorrow is a mystery. Today is a gift. That is why we call it the present.

-Alice Morse Earle

Reflection

What does living in the present mean to you? Do you live your life this way?

_____

_____

_____

_____

_____

_____

_____

_____

_____

_____

_____

_____

_____

Intention

What is your intention for today? Just for today...

_____

_____

_____

Meditation

How long did you meditate today? What type of meditation did you complete? Journal about today's meditation experience.

_____

_____

_____

Gratitude
Which three things are you grateful for today?

_____

_____

_____

Reading
Write one thought from today's reading that was meaningful to you.

_____

_____

_____

Exercise
Record how you chose to exercise today.

_____

_____

_____

Affirmations
Write three affirmations for today.

_____

_____

_____

Time for Self-Care
Reflect on what you did today to nourish your soul.

_____

_____

_____

How would you rate today?
1   2   3   4   5   6   7   8   9   10

Change your thoughts and you change your world.
-Norman Vincent Peale

Reflection

What thoughts do you need to change in order to see a transformation in your life?

_____
_____
_____
_____
_____
_____
_____
_____
_____
_____
_____
_____
_____
_____

Intention

What is your intention for today? Just for today...

_____
_____
_____

Meditation

How long did you meditate today? What type of meditation did you complete? Journal about today's meditation experience.

_____
_____
_____

Gratitude

Which three things are you grateful for today?

_____

_____

Reading

Write one thought from today's reading that was meaningful to you.

_____

_____

Exercise

Record how you chose to exercise today.

_____

_____

Affirmations

Write three affirmations for today.

_____

_____

Time for Self-Care

Reflect on what you did today to nourish your soul.

_____

_____

How would you rate today?   1   2   3   4   5   6   7   8   9   10

Don't live the same year 75 times and call it a life.
  -Robin Sharma

Reflection

Do you live your life by routine or spontaneity? Try doing the opposite today and write about your experience.

_____
_____
_____
_____
_____
_____
_____
_____
_____
_____
_____
_____
_____
_____
_____

Intention

What is your intention for today? Just for today...

_____
_____

Meditation

How long did you meditate today? What type of meditation did you complete? Journal about today's meditation experience.

_____
_____
_____

Gratitude

Which three things are you grateful for today?

_____

_____

_____

Reading

Write one thought from today's reading that was meaningful to you.

_____

_____

_____

Exercise

Record how you chose to exercise today.

_____

_____

_____

Affirmations

Write three affirmations for today.

_____

_____

_____

Time for Self-Care

Reflect on what you did today to nourish your soul.

_____

_____

_____

How would you rate today?

1   2   3   4   5   6   7   8   9   10

Change can either challenge us or threaten us. Your beliefs pave your way to success or block you.

-Marsha Sinetar

Reflection

Are your beliefs moving you forward or holding you back? Are you willing to change your beliefs in order to gain success?

_____

_____

_____

_____

_____

_____

_____

_____

_____

_____

_____

_____

_____

_____

_____

Intention

What is your intention for today? Just for today...

_____

_____

Meditation

How long did you meditate today? What type of meditation did you complete? Journal about today's meditation experience.

_____

_____

_____

Gratitude

Which three things are you grateful for today?

_____

_____

Reading

Write one thought from today's reading that was meaningful to you.

_____

_____

Exercise

Record how you chose to exercise today.

_____

_____

Affirmations

Write three affirmations for today.

_____

_____

Time for Self-Care

Reflect on what you did today to nourish your soul.

_____

_____

How would you rate today?   1   2   3   4   5   6   7   8   9   10

Discipline is doing what needs to be done even if you don't want to do it.

-Anonymous

Reflection

What are you most disciplined about in your life and why?

_____

_____

_____

_____

_____

_____

_____

_____

_____

_____

_____

_____

_____

_____

Intention

What is your intention for today? Just for today...

_____

_____

Meditation

How long did you meditate today? What type of meditation did you complete? Journal about today's meditation experience.

_____

_____

_____

Gratitude

Which three things are you grateful for today?

_____

_____

Reading

Write one thought from today's reading that was meaningful to you.

_____

_____

Exercise

Record how you chose to exercise today.

_____

_____

Affirmations

Write three affirmations for today.

_____

_____

Time for Self-Care

Reflect on what you did today to nourish your soul.

_____

_____

How would you rate today?

1   2   3   4   5   6   7   8   9   10

Even if you are on the right path, you'll get run over if you just sit there.

-Will Rogers

Reflection

Describe a time when you were on the right path. Where did the path take you?

_____

_____

_____

_____

_____

_____

_____

_____

_____

_____

_____

_____

_____

_____

_____

_____

Intention

What is your intention for today? Just for today...

_____

_____

Meditation

How long did you meditate today? What type of meditation did you complete? Journal about today's meditation experience.

_____

_____

_____

Gratitude

Which three things are you grateful for today?

_____

_____

_____

Reading

Write one thought from today's reading that was meaningful to you.

_____

_____

_____

Exercise

Record how you chose to exercise today.

_____

_____

_____

Affirmations

Write three affirmations for today.

_____

_____

_____

Time for Self-Care

Reflect on what you did today to nourish your soul.

_____

_____

_____

How would you rate today?   1   2   3   4   5   6   7   8   9   10

A person who never made a mistake never tried anything new.

-Albert Einstein

Reflection

Describe something positive that came from a mistake you once made.

_____

_____

_____

_____

_____

_____

_____

_____

_____

_____

_____

_____

_____

_____

Intention

What is your intention for today? Just for today...

_____

_____

Meditation

How long did you meditate today? What type of meditation did you complete? Journal about today's meditation experience.

_____

_____

_____

Gratitude

Which three things are you grateful for today?

_____

_____

_____

Reading

Write one thought from today's reading that was meaningful to you.

_____

_____

_____

Exercise

Record how you chose to exercise today.

_____

_____

_____

Affirmations

Write three affirmations for today.

_____

_____

_____

Time for Self-Care

Reflect on what you did today to nourish your soul.

_____

_____

_____

How would you rate today?   1   2   3   4   5   6   7   8   9   10

Every day is a new beginning. Take a deep breath. Smile and start again.

-Anonymous

Reflection

How do you typically begin your day?

_____

_____

_____

_____

_____

_____

_____

_____

_____

_____

_____

_____

_____

Intention

What is your intention for today? Just for today...

_____

_____

_____

Meditation

How long did you meditate today? What type of meditation did you complete? Journal about today's meditation experience.

_____

_____

_____

Gratitude

Which three things are you grateful for today?

_____

_____

_____

Reading

Write one thought from today's reading that was meaningful to you.

_____

_____

_____

Exercise

Record how you chose to exercise today.

_____

_____

_____

Affirmations

Write three affirmations for today.

_____

_____

_____

Time for Self-Care

Reflect on what you did today to nourish your soul.

_____

_____

_____

How would you rate today?   1   2   3   4   5   6   7   8   9   10

A journey of a thousand miles begins with a single step.
-Lao Tzu

Reflection

Describe a journey in your life that began with a single step. Where did your journey take you?

_____

_____

_____

_____

_____

_____

_____

_____

_____

_____

_____

_____

_____

_____

Intention

What is your intention for today? Just for today...

_____

_____

Meditation

How long did you meditate today? What type of meditation did you complete? Journal about today's meditation experience.

_____

_____

_____

Gratitude

Which three things are you grateful for today?

_____

_____

_____

Reading

Write one thought from today's reading that was meaningful to you.

_____

_____

_____

Exercise

Record how you chose to exercise today.

_____

_____

_____

Affirmations

Write three affirmations for today.

_____

_____

_____

Time for Self-Care

Reflect on what you did today to nourish your soul.

_____

_____

_____

How would you rate today?   1   2   3   4   5   6   7   8   9   10

There will never be as much time in your life as there is now.
-Anonymous

Reflection

Create a bucket list of what you want to do with the rest of your life. Choose one thing to do today and write about it.

_____
_____
_____
_____
_____
_____
_____
_____
_____
_____
_____
_____
_____
_____
_____
_____

Intention

What is your intention for today? Just for today...

_____
_____

Meditation

How long did you meditate today? What type of meditation did you complete? Journal about today's meditation experience.

_____
_____
_____

Gratitude

Which three things are you grateful for today?

_____

_____

Reading

Write one thought from today's reading that was meaningful to you.

_____

_____

Exercise

Record how you chose to exercise today.

_____

_____

Affirmations

Write three affirmations for today.

_____

_____

Time for Self-Care

Reflect on what you did today to nourish your soul.

_____

_____

How would you rate today?

1   2   3   4   5   6   7   8   9   10

Perseverance is stubbornness with a purpose.
-Josh Shipp

Reflection

Describe a time when your perseverance paid off.

_____

_____

_____

_____

_____

_____

_____

_____

_____

_____

_____

_____

_____

_____

_____

_____

Intention

What is your intention for today? Just for today...

_____

_____

Meditation

How long did you meditate today? What type of meditation did you complete? Journal about today's meditation experience.

_____

_____

_____

Gratitude

Which three things are you grateful for today?

_____

_____

_____

Reading

Write one thought from today's reading that was meaningful to you.

_____

_____

_____

Exercise

Record how you chose to exercise today.

_____

_____

_____

Affirmations

Write three affirmations for today.

_____

_____

_____

Time for Self-Care

Reflect on what you did today to nourish your soul.

_____

_____

_____

How would you rate today?

1   2   3   4   5   6   7   8   9   10

A mistake repeated more than once is a decision.
-Paulo Coelho

Reflection

What mistake have you made more than once? What do you need to do differently to avoid making the same mistake again?

_____

_____

_____

_____

_____

_____

_____

_____

_____

_____

_____

_____

_____

_____

_____

_____

_____

Intention

What is your intention for today? Just for today...

_____

_____

Meditation

How long did you meditate today? What type of meditation did you complete? Journal about today's meditation experience.

_____

_____

_____

Gratitude

Which three things are you grateful for today?

_____

_____

_____

Reading

Write one thought from today's reading that was meaningful to you.

_____

_____

_____

Exercise

Record how you chose to exercise today.

_____

_____

_____

Affirmations

Write three affirmations for today.

_____

_____

_____

Time for Self-Care

Reflect on what you did today to nourish your soul.

_____

_____

_____

How would you rate today?

1   2   3   4   5   6   7   8   9   10

Surround yourself with people who encourage you, inspire you, and believe in your dreams.

-Anonymous

Reflection

Who are the people who believe in you? How have they supported you?

_____

_____

_____

_____

_____

_____

_____

_____

_____

_____

_____

_____

_____

_____

Intention

What is your intention for today? Just for today...

_____

_____

Meditation

How long did you meditate today? What type of meditation did you complete? Journal about today's meditation experience.

_____

_____

_____

Gratitude

Which three things are you grateful for today?

_____

_____

Reading

Write one thought from today's reading that was meaningful to you.

_____

_____

Exercise

Record how you chose to exercise today.

_____

_____

Affirmations

Write three affirmations for today.

_____

_____

Time for Self-Care

Reflect on what you did today to nourish your soul.

_____

_____

How would you rate today?

1   2   3   4   5   6   7   8   9   10

Take Time to Reflect

YOU ARE AMAZING! Look how far you've come on your journey of self-discovery.

Describe the transformation that you have seen in yourself since beginning your journey. What positive changes have you noticed?

Even though your journey with this book will soon be over, I hope that you will continue to set goals for yourself and work toward your dreams. Always keep striving to create a better version of yourself!

_____

_____

_____

_____

_____

_____

_____

_____

_____

_____

_____

_____

_____

_____

_____

_____

_____

_____

Never regret
a day in your life;

good days give
happiness,

bad days give
experience,

worst days give
lessons,

and best days give
memories.

Conclusion

Life is a game, play it. Life is a challenge, meet it. Life is an opportunity, capture it.

-Anonymous

Life is a journey. Three months ago you embarked on a journey of self-discovery with *I'M GREAT Every Day: A Guided Journal for Creating a Better Self* and now here you stand, almost at the end of this journey. Congratulations on your accomplishment!

As you journaled through the pages of this book, I'm sure there were days you felt happy, sad, afraid, grateful, or angry. Along the way, you discovered both your strengths and your weaknesses. You most likely discovered truths about yourself that were not easy to accept. However, it is only in our acceptance of these truths that we are able to grow in mind, body, heart, and spirit and, in turn, become a better version of who we are.

Life will always be filled with challenges, but your reactions to these challenges will play a bigger role in your life than the challenges themselves. It is your reactions to these challenges that will help shape you into the person you will become. Challenges enable us to learn, to grow, and to find our strength. Without them we cannot know what we are capable of.

Learn to let go of what you cannot control so that you can make the most of what every day has to offer. None of us know how much time we have left on this earth, so learn to be happy now. Spend time with the people that are important to you and find the time to do what makes you happy.

I'd like to take a moment now to offer you my sincere thanks in allowing *I'M GREAT Every Day: A Guided Journal for Creating a Better Self* to be a part of your self-discovery. True transformation only comes when we learn to love and accept ourselves for the unique individuals that we are. I hope your journey through this book provided you with the personal growth you were seeking when you first began. Most importantly, I hope that as a result of this journey, you have come to discover how truly amazing you are. There is no one else like you.

To celebrate your completion of this journal, I have included a special gift for you. In the remaining pages, you will find ten additional prompts along with an additional vision board. Think about where you want to be a year from now or perhaps even five years from now. Use this bonus vision board to outline the steps you'll need to take to make your dream of today your reality for tomorrow.

If you would like to share your story or tell me how *I'M GREAT Every Day: A Guided Journal for Creating a Better Self* has made a positive impact on your life, I would love to hear from you.

Thank you once again for allowing *I'M GREAT Every Day: A Guided Journal for Creating a Better Self* to be a part of your soul-searching experience.

Connect with Me

imgreateveryday@gmail.com
linda-callahan.com

With much love and respect,

Linda Callahan

My **Goal Setting** *Worksheet*

Today's Date _____   Goal Completion Date _____

My goal is (be as specific as you can): _____

_____

_____

These are the steps I will need to take in order to achieve my goal:

1. _____

2. _____

3. _____

4. _____

When I am discouraged, I will remind myself why it's important to achieve this goal.

I want to achieve this goal because_____

_____

_____

I will track my progress here _____

_____

_____

When I achieve my goal, I will _____

_____

_____

S.M.A.R.T. GOALS *Worksheet*

Specific	What exactly do you want to accomplish?
Measurable	How will you track your progress?
Attainable	Do you have the skills and resources to attain this goal? What steps do you need to take to achieve your goal?
Relevant	Why is this goal important to you?
Timely	When do you want to complete this goal?

Create Your Vision Board

This just may be your most important vision board yet! Let's fast forward to a year from now or even five years from now. What are your goals for the future? What steps will you need to take today to make your dreams happen?

You can use the box on the opposite page to practice your design. Then you can create the vision board on the following pages.

I sincerely hope all of your dreams come true because life is too short for any of us to live our lives with someone else's dream. Start living your dreams NOW!

BOARD

Everything in your life is a reflection of a choice you have made. If you want a different result, make a different choice.

-Anonymous

Reflection

Describe a poor decision you made and explain what happened as a result.

_____

_____

_____

_____

_____

_____

_____

_____

_____

_____

_____

_____

_____

Intention

What is your intention for today? Just for today...

_____

_____

Meditation

How long did you meditate today? What type of meditation did you complete? Journal about today's meditation experience.

_____

_____

_____

Gratitude

Which three things are you grateful for today?

_____

_____

_____

Reading

Write one thought from today's reading that was meaningful to you.

_____

_____

_____

Exercise

Record how you chose to exercise today.

_____

_____

_____

Affirmations

Write three affirmations for today.

_____

_____

_____

Time for Self-Care

Reflect on what you did today to nourish your soul.

_____

_____

_____

How would you rate today?   1   2   3   4   5   6   7   8   9   10

You must gain control of your money or the lack of it will always control you.

-Dave Ramsey

Reflection

Are you a saver or a spender? How well do you budget your money?

_____

_____

_____

_____

_____

_____

_____

_____

_____

_____

_____

_____

_____

Intention

What is your intention for today? Just for today...

_____

_____

Meditation

How long did you meditate today? What type of meditation did you complete? Journal about today's meditation experience.

_____

_____

_____

Gratitude

Which three things are you grateful for today?

_____

_____

_____

Reading

Write one thought from today's reading that was meaningful to you.

_____

_____

_____

Exercise

Record how you chose to exercise today.

_____

_____

_____

Affirmations

Write three affirmations for today.

_____

_____

_____

Time for Self-Care

Reflect on what you did today to nourish your soul.

_____

_____

_____

How would you rate today?

1   2   3   4   5   6   7   8   9   10

Depending on what they are, our habits will either make us or break us. We become what we repeatedly do.
-Sean Covey

Reflection

Which habits do you need to change and why?

_____

_____

_____

_____

_____

_____

_____

_____

_____

_____

_____

_____

_____

_____

Intention

What is your intention for today? Just for today...

_____

_____

Meditation

How long did you meditate today? What type of meditation did you complete? Journal about today's meditation experience.

_____

_____

_____

Gratitude

Which three things are you grateful for today?

_____

_____

Reading

Write one thought from today's reading that was meaningful to you.

_____

_____

Exercise

Record how you chose to exercise today.

_____

_____

Affirmations

Write three affirmations for today.

_____

_____

Time for Self-Care

Reflect on what you did today to nourish your soul.

_____

_____

How would you rate today?   1   2   3   4   5   6   7   8   9   10

Love is when the other person's happiness is more important than your own.
-H. Jackson Brown, Jr.

Reflection

Write about a time when you put someone else's happiness before your own.

_____
_____
_____
_____
_____
_____
_____
_____
_____
_____
_____
_____
_____
_____
_____
_____

Intention

What is your intention for today? Just for today...

_____
_____

Meditation

How long did you meditate today? What type of meditation did you complete? Journal about today's meditation experience.

_____
_____
_____

Gratitude
Which three things are you grateful for today?

_____

_____

_____

Reading
Write one thought from today's reading that was meaningful to you.

_____

_____

_____

Exercise
Record how you chose to exercise today.

_____

_____

_____

Affirmations
Write three affirmations for today.

_____

_____

_____

Time for Self-Care
Reflect on what you did today to nourish your soul.

_____

_____

_____

How would you rate today?
1   2   3   4   5   6   7   8   9   10

There should be no discrimination against languages people speak, skin color, or religion.

-Malala Yousafzai

Reflection

Write about a time when you felt discriminated against.

_____

_____

_____

_____

_____

_____

_____

_____

_____

_____

_____

_____

_____

_____

_____

_____

Intention

What is your intention for today? Just for today...

_____

_____

Meditation

How long did you meditate today? What type of meditation did you complete? Journal about today's meditation experience.

_____

_____

_____

Gratitude

Which three things are you grateful for today?

_____

_____

Reading

Write one thought from today's reading that was meaningful to you.

_____

_____

Exercise

Record how you chose to exercise today.

_____

_____

Affirmations

Write three affirmations for today.

_____

_____

Time for Self-Care

Reflect on what you did today to nourish your soul.

_____

_____

How would you rate today?   1   2   3   4   5   6   7   8   9   10

Pets leave paw prints on your heart.

-Anonymous

Reflection

Have you ever owned a pet? If so, how did having a pet enrich your life? If not, explain why you never had a pet. Is there a pet you wish you could have owned?

_____

_____

_____

_____

_____

_____

_____

_____

_____

_____

_____

_____

_____

Intention

What is your intention for today? Just for today...

_____

_____

_____

Meditation

How long did you meditate today? What type of meditation did you complete? Journal about today's meditation experience.

_____

_____

_____

Gratitude
Which three things are you grateful for today?

_____
_____
_____

Reading
Write one thought from today's reading that was meaningful to you.

_____
_____
_____

Exercise
Record how you chose to exercise today.

_____
_____
_____

Affirmations
Write three affirmations for today.

_____
_____
_____

Time for Self-Care
Reflect on what you did today to nourish your soul.

_____
_____
_____

How would you rate today?
1   2   3   4   5   6   7   8   9   10

Volunteers are not paid, not because they are worthless, but because they are priceless.

-Anonymous

Reflection

Describe a time when you volunteered. How did you feel afterwards?

_____

_____

_____

_____

_____

_____

_____

_____

_____

_____

_____

_____

_____

_____

Intention

What is your intention for today? Just for today...

_____

_____

Meditation

How long did you meditate today? What type of meditation did you complete? Journal about today's meditation experience.

_____

_____

_____

Gratitude

Which three things are you grateful for today?

_____

_____

Reading

Write one thought from today's reading that was meaningful to you.

_____

_____

Exercise

Record how you chose to exercise today.

_____

_____

Affirmations

Write three affirmations for today.

_____

_____

Time for Self-Care

Reflect on what you did today to nourish your soul.

_____

_____

_____

How would you rate today?

1   2   3   4   5   6   7   8   9   10

You can't go back and change the beginning, but you can start where you are and change the ending.

-C.S. Lewis

Reflection

What can you begin doing differently today to create a better tomorrow?

_____

_____

_____

_____

_____

_____

_____

_____

_____

_____

_____

_____

_____

_____

Intention

What is your intention for today? Just for today...

_____

_____

Meditation

How long did you meditate today? What type of meditation did you complete? Journal about today's meditation experience.

_____

_____

_____

Gratitude
Which three things are you grateful for today?

_____

_____

Reading
Write one thought from today's reading that was meaningful to you.

_____

_____

Exercise
Record how you chose to exercise today.

_____

_____

Affirmations
Write three affirmations for today.

_____

_____

Time for Self-Care
Reflect on what you did today to nourish your soul.

_____

_____

How would you rate today?   1   2   3   4   5   6   7   8   9   10

Home is said to be the starting place of love, hope, and dreams.
-Anonymous

Reflection

The word *home* means something different to each of us. What does the word *home* mean to you?

_____

_____

_____

_____

_____

_____

_____

_____

_____

_____

_____

_____

_____

Intention

What is your intention for today? Just for today...

_____

_____

Meditation

How long did you meditate today? What type of meditation did you complete? Journal about today's meditation experience.

_____

_____

_____

Gratitude

Which three things are you grateful for today?

_____

_____

_____

Reading

Write one thought from today's reading that was meaningful to you.

_____

_____

_____

Exercise

Record how you chose to exercise today.

_____

_____

_____

Affirmations

Write three affirmations for today.

_____

_____

_____

Time for Self-Care

Reflect on what you did today to nourish your soul.

_____

_____

_____

How would you rate today?

1   2   3   4   5   6   7   8   9   10

Wake up every morning with the thought that something wonderful is about to happen.

-Anonymous

Reflection

Describe something wonderful that happened today.

_____

_____

_____

_____

_____

_____

_____

_____

_____

_____

_____

_____

_____

_____

_____

_____

Intention

What is your intention for today? Just for today...

_____

_____

_____

Meditation

How long did you meditate today? What type of meditation did you complete? Journal about today's meditation experience.

_____

_____

_____

Gratitude

Which three things are you grateful for today?

_____

_____

Reading

Write one thought from today's reading that was meaningful to you.

_____

_____

Exercise

Record how you chose to exercise today.

_____

_____

Affirmations

Write three affirmations for today.

_____

_____

Time for Self-Care

Reflect on what you did today to nourish your soul.

_____

_____

How would you rate today?

1   2   3   4   5   6   7   8   9   10

Take Time to Reflect

As you prepare to write your final reflection page, know that you are not the same person you were when you first began this adventure. Use what you have learned about yourself over the last three months to write your final thoughts.

True transformation takes time. Just as the caterpillar must go through several changes before it can transform into the beautiful butterfly it was always destined to be, you will also go through several changes before you become the person you were always meant to be. And in time, you too, will spread your wings and fly.

YOU ARE GREAT! You always have been; it's just taken you a little longer to figure that out for yourself. You are destined for wonder. The Universe is waiting to give you everything you deserve.

Take a few minutes now to journal about the discoveries you have made. How will you use the knowledge you learned about yourself to grow into the person you were always meant to be?

_____

_____

_____

_____

_____

_____

_____

_____

_____

_____

_____

_____

_____

_____

Suggested Reading List

I've always had a passion for reading. There never seems to be enough time in any given day for the amount of books I want to read. Reading allows us the opportunity to learn and grow. Reading empowers your mind and feeds your soul, allowing what you've read to become an eternal part of you.

I'd like to recommend some of my favorite book titles to you with the hope that you'll not only enjoy reading them as much as I did, but that you, too, will learn and grow from them.

Happy reading.

My Morning Routine Reading Books

Beattie, Melody. *Journey to the Heart: Daily Meditations on the Path to Freeing Your Soul.* New York: HarperCollins, 1996.

Breathnach, Sarah Ban. *Simple Abundance: A Daybook of Comfort and Joy.* New York: Warner Books, Inc., 1995.

Howell, Angela. Finding the Gift: Daily Meditations for Mindfulness. The United States of America: 2015.

Dao, Deng Ming. *365 Tao: Daily Meditations.* New York: Harper Collins, 1992.

Siegel, Bernie S. *365 Prescriptions for the Soul: Daily Messages of Inspiration, Hope, and Love.* California: New World Library, 2004

D'Simone,Sah. *5-Minute Daily Meditations: Instant Wisdom, Clarity & Calm.* California: Althea Press, 2018

Spiegel, Cyndie. *A Year of Positive Thinking: Daily Inspiration, Wisdom, and Courage.* California: Althea Press, 2018

Additional Resources

The following is a list of personal development books that have made a positive influence in my life. I think they will make a positive influence in your life as well.

Anderson, Joan. *A Walk on the Beach.* New York: Broadway Books, 2004.

Anderson, Joan. *A Weekend to Change Your Life: Find Your Authentic Self After a Lifetime of Being All Things to All People.* New York: Broadway Books, 2006.

Anderson, Joan. *A Year by the Sea: Thoughts of an Unfinished Woman.* New York: Broadway Books, 1996.

Andrews, Andy. *The Noticer.* Tennessee: W. Publishing, an imprint of Thomas Nelson, 2009.

Byrne, Rhonda. *The Secret.* New York: Atria Books, 2006.

Cahn, Luann. *I Dare Me.* New York: Penguin Book, 2013.

Cameron, Julia. *The Artist's Way: A Spiritual path to Higher Creativity.* New York: Penguin Random House, 1992, 2002, 2016.

Canfield, Jack. *The Success Principles: How to Get from Where You Are to Where You Want to Be.* New York: William Morrow, 2015.

Elrod, Hal. *The Miracle Morning: The Not-So-Obvious Secret Guaranteed to Transform Your Life Before 8am.* The United States of America: Hal Elrod International, Inc., 2016.

Hay, Louis. *You Can Heal Your Life.* New York: Hay House, Inc., 1984, 1987, 2004.

Kelly, Matthew: *The Rhythm of Life: Living Everyday with Passion and Purpose.* Florida: Beacon Publishing, 1999.

Lindbergh, Anne Morrow. *Gift from the Sea.* New York: Pantheon Books, 1955, 1975, 1983, 2003.

Robbins, Mel. *The 5 Second Rule: Transform Your Life, Work, and Confidence with Everyday Courage.* The United States of America: Savio Republic, 2017.

Sincero, Jen. *You are a Badass: How to Stop Doubting Your Greatness and Start Living an Awesome Life.* Philadelphia, Pa: Running Press, 2013.

Endings often
disguise themselves as
new beginnings.

Today you will
close the door to your past
and start the next chapter
of your life.

Remember, the best is yet to come!

CPSIA information can be obtained
at www.ICGtesting.com
Printed in the USA
BVHW070834050921
615739BV00002B/6

9 780578 860527